Making and Repairing
WESTERN SADDLES

Making and Repairing
WESTERN SADDLES

Dave Jones

PRENTICE
HALL PRESS
EQUESTRIAN
BOOKS

PRENTICE HALL PRESS

New York   London   Toronto   Sydney   Tokyo   Singapore

Published in 1987 by Prentice Hall Press
A Division of Simon & Schuster, Inc.
15 Columbus Circle
New York, NY 10023

Originally published by Arco Publishing, Inc.

PRENTICE HALL PRESS is a trademark of Simon & Schuster, Inc.

Library of Congress Cataloging-in-Publication Data

Jones, Dave, 1927-
    Making and repairing western saddles.
    Includes index.
    1. Saddlery.   I. Title.
TS1032.J77   685.1   81-19106
ISBN 0-668-04906-5

Manufactured in the United States of America

10 9 8 7 6

Contents

Foreword

To those who use them, saddles can stir vivid memories of the Old West. After much thought, many a rider has developed the urge to make a saddle for his own personal use. To those with a little experience in leather work, making a saddle looks easy. It is not the case. When he's ready to start his project, the amateur saddlemaker will run into multiple problems. What materials will he need and where will he get them? What tools will he need and where will he get these? And after those two problems, he's face to face with the big one: how and where does he start? If you're that rider, this book will come to your aid with all the answers. It will tell you what to do and how to do it.

Over the years, several books have been published on the making of saddles and horse gear. Most of these have been slanted either to the amateur who wants to make a saddle for his own personal use or to the journeyman saddlemaker who has spent years at the saddler's bench. You never get too old to learn something new about a job—even one you've worked at a long time.

With his background of many years experience as a horsetrainer and saddlemaker, Dave Jones has succeeded in writing a book from which both the amateur and professional saddlemaker can profit. It will give the amateur the "what and where" he needs to start the job, and, hopefully, it will supply the "something new" for the journeyman saddlemaker with years of experience; for example, the all-leather ground seat, first used by D. E. Walker in his Visalia shop back in 1870. This type of ground seat was used in all Walker saddles till the firm closed their business about 1960. Walker saddles even after thirty years of hard ranch work, were found to still have firm seats. Today, the all-leather ground seat is seldom used outside of California.

In addition, few professional saddlemakers have all the tools they need. From this book, you just might find the source of a tool you've been looking for for a long, long time.

This book combines informal text with many illustrations that, after careful study, will help you overcome most saddle-making problems. It covers the field of saddle making from the bare tree to the finished product.

Lee Rice

Preface

Back in 1949 I wintered with Jack Link, a top horseman and saddlemaker. I watched him build a couple of saddles and tried to remember the steps. I learned how to sew leather from him and how to do a lot of the leatherwork that must be done to keep gear in shape.

A few years ago a millionaire rode one of my beat up ole bronc saddles and said that although he had a roomful of saddles, none rode as good as my ole rig. This started me thinking about making saddles for sale. Till then, the only reason I made saddles at all was that I couldn't buy what I wanted.

I started making saddles back in the late 1950s. The first of these featured forward-hung stirrups and a fairly level seat. My first saddles had the ride I wanted, but they were uncomfortable. One rider told me they felt like they came with built-in rocks.

Some time later I got a copy of Bruce Grant's book, *How to Make Cowboy Horse Gear*, which has a section on western saddlemaking by Lee M. Rice. (I recently read a book that mentioned Lee M. Rice as the dean of saddlemakers.) I started making my saddles with the all-leather ground seat as described by Mr. Rice, and the way they rode improved dramatically—immediately. I never again put in a metal ground seat, though I do think that I could put one in now that'd ride pretty fair. The millionaire rode one with the all-leather ground seat.

I've corresponded with Mr. Rice and he gave me the lowdown on all this. The leather ground seat originated at the Dave E. Walker saddle shop in San Francisco. Only men who worked there used this method. Of course, some quit or were fired and established their own saddle shops elsewhere. But the all-leather ground seat never achieved widespread use because few saddlemakers knew how to put it in correctly, and it took a lot more time to install than the metal ground seat.

When Jack Lewis, then editor of *Horse and Rider*, reviewed my book *Practical Western Training*, he said, "Dave Jones either knows more about training than the others or tells more."

Perhaps I do have some ability at explanation. I hope that maybe this book will offer something to the beginner. Maybe I can explain the tools and techniques, so that a guy can make a decent saddle the first try.

No saddlemaker can turn out good work if he has a poor tree. He gets a tree and fits it with leather, so that the style suits the rider and makes life pleasant for the horse. So let's give the tree makers the credit they deserve, for we couldn't survive without them.

There are reasons for custom saddles. The rider who orders one gets what he wants—if he knows what he wants when he puts in his order. If you buy a production-line saddle, you buy what's already made. You have to get used to it.

A custom saddlemaker takes your order and *then* orders the saddle tree. If you want a level-ride saddle, he'll make it that way. He makes patterns as he goes—fits, skives, glues, nails, and sews the pieces into place.

A production-line saddle company orders three thousand trees. Many have their own tree factory. A tree *may* be wood and rawhide but it also may be covered with fiberglass or canvas. Parts are stamped out and tooled. Assembly is like Detroit. Most of the sewing is done on a machine. The ground seat may be a tin strainer covered with flimsy felt, such as that used under carpets.

When I get done buying the leather, sheepskin, tree, rigging, stirrups, and stirrups-buckles for a custom saddle, the cost is about $300. But you can find new production-line saddles cheaper than $300. You get value for your money in a production-line saddle, but if you want what you want—and quality—try a good custom saddle.

There are, of course, saddles made up for sale of excellent quality, but the price is right up there with the custom saddle.

In this book we'll use no machines. The whole saddle will be made by hand. When I make a plain saddle, it takes me about a month of night work. I'd spend less time if I could make saddles during the days. In actual time I'd say that a plain saddle can be made in fifty hours or less.

I write first thing in the morning, handle horses during the day, and go to the saddle shop at night.

Making and Repairing
WESTERN SADDLES

1

Tools and Materials

I think most saddlemakers like tools and buy anything new they hear about, so a list is always incomplete. Most of the common hand tools are readily available. Some tools can be purchased from custom toolmakers. The handy guy can make a lot of his own tools. And you'll find tools that can be purchased from other saddlemakers. There's always a way.

Knives The saddlemaker needs good sharp knives—for he's always cutting and skiving. The round knife is essential, for it's both a cutting knife and a skiving knife. The straight knife is used for many things. The shoemaker's lip knife can be used for cutting leather around the fork. The Osborne round knives are pretty good; buy the largest that you can use comfortably. There are a few custom knifemakers who turn out excellent knives.

I recently bought some knives from a fine Montana knifemaker, L. B. Lienemann. These knives came ready to use—extremely sharp. He has over twenty patterns for round knives and a couple of patterns for straight knives. The steel for the larger knives is $^1/_{16}$-inch thick, while the steel for the smaller knives is $^3/_{64}$-inch thick. Or, I should say, thin.

I asked Mr. Lienemann how he got his knives so sharp. He has converted a lathe to hold several hard felt wheels. Different abrasive grits are applied to these wheels. They cut the metal down and polish it. They are ground down very thin at the edge. Then he uses different grades of Arkansas stones, finishing off with a strop impregnated with jeweler's rouge.

Alan Dewey, my apprentice trainer and expert saddlemaker, favors a sander-grinder for thinning metal down. After a few months he convinced me.

These sander-grinders are really something. They come with belts from 60 grit (coarse) to 500 grit (very fine). The medium grit works best for me. I soon cut down my old thick knives; it made all the difference in the world in their cutting ability.

There are many uses for the grinder. It'll sharpen a lawn-mower blade, axes, or anything else you'd use around the place. When a wheel is used, you're apt to burn up the metal and do a wavy, uneven job. With the grinder you have a flat surface to work on, which is over a foot long. Since you want to bevel and flatten edges, this is the tool to do it with.

Cutting Boards and Surfaces When you're cutting leather, you need a grainless surface to cut on because you may ruin some leather or knock the point of your knife off if the knife grabs the board. A piece of Masonite provides a good cutting

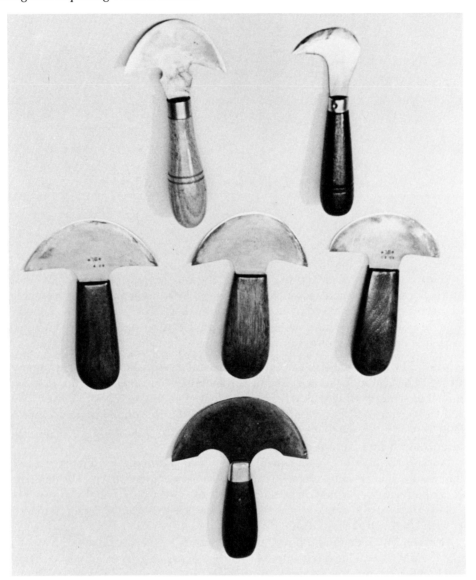

Round knives. Top left: *small Dixon knife.* Top right: *Osborne head knife.* Center: *L.B. Lienemann round knives.* Bottom: *Osborne knife.*

surface. You can use both sides of it, though the rough side is best. I have a piece of high-density polyethylene, which is excellent, though expensive. Check with your local plastic company about it. Butchers use this high-density poly. Yours can get a piece for you—but make sure that you have plenty of money in your checkbook when ordering.

Knife-Sharpening Tools The sander-grinder thins knives down. Once they're thinned, you need to keep them sharp. Knives should be razor-sharp at all times—you'll mess up leather with dull tools.

The Arkansas stones can't be beat. Medium grade is OK. The soft one really cuts. Always use honing fluid with them.

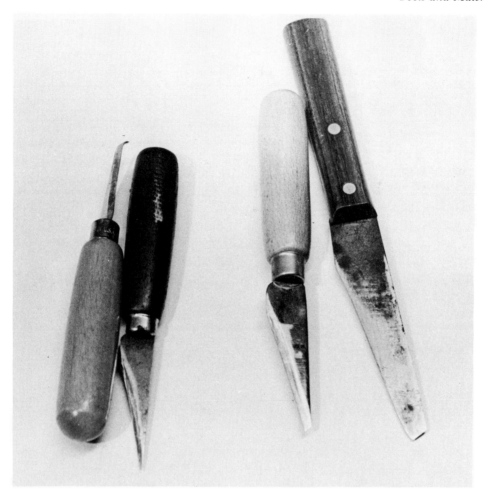

Leather knives. Left to right: *large skiving knife; utility knives; lip knife with blunt point.*

I recently bought a hard felt wheel and abrasive compound.

Ten seconds honing on this tool really puts an edge on the knives. I keep this wheel on my bench all the time.

You can't beat a razor strop. You can buy jeweler's rouge from Tandy. It comes in stick form; rub it into your strop. This puts the final edge on your knives. Tandy stores are located in most major cities.

Flat and Curved Edgers   Most parts of the saddle should have the edges beveled. This is cosmetic but it's always done. Use an edge beveler for this. Probably the best edgers available for the saddlemaker are the larger Osborne western edgers. Of course you may like another type. Edgers are not really expensive—try some different styles. They can be sharpened with small slipstones and jeweler's files. Woodcraft catalogs list the slipstones and your jeweler can tell you where to get the files. To put the finishing edge on them, strop them on a leather shoestring rubbed with jeweler's rouge. You can also use cord for this.

Flat edgers (French edgers) are mostly used for skiving edges. When you skive down the edge of the stirrup strap where it's riveted onto the fender, for instance, you use a French edger to clean the edge. Edgers also cut pretty well. Mr.

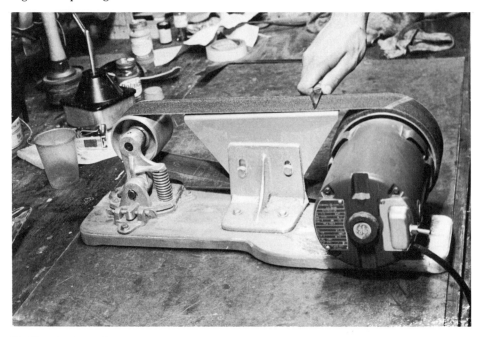

Knifemaker's sander-grinder.

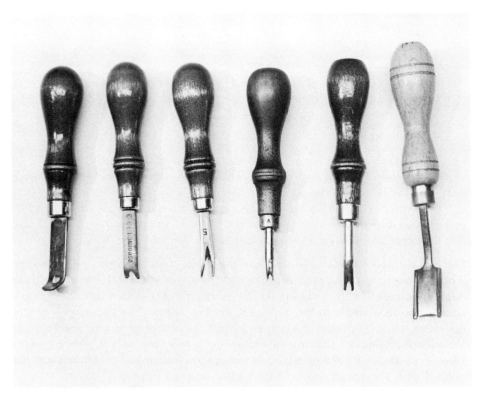

Edgers. Left to right: *Bisonette, western, common, small Rampart, larger Rampart, large French.*

Rice suggests cutting out the seat around the saddle fork with a French edger. There are many uses for these tools, which you'll discover after you really get into saddle work. They can be sharpened on an oilstone, on the hard felt wheel and they can be stropped.

Stitching Groovers and Markers

Sewing tools are very important since we do so much hand stitching. It's important to keep the stitches below the surface of the leather. Where there's a lot of wear, stitches should be pulled down deeply into the leather. To do this, first thoroughly soak the leather in water and case it (keep in a bag or tight drawer to preserve moisture. See page 25 for casing instructions). Cut a groove in the leather with a stitching groover. Then roll a stitch marker along the groove. These markers come in different sizes, such as a #5, #6, or #7. This means that the marker makes five, six, or seven marks to the inch. For ordinary saddle work we use five marks per inch. For fancy stuff, we use six per inch.

An Osborne groover features two grooving loops and a scratcher. This is probably the best groover on the market.

Sewing Awls   There are various types of awls. You will want the awl haft to feel good to you. Some awl hafts have chucks, which allow the awl blade to be changed.

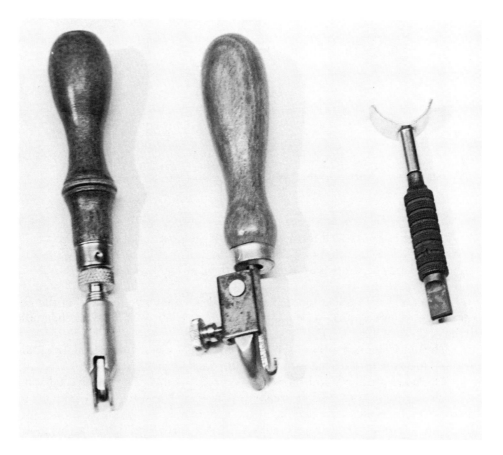

Stitching groovers. Left to right: *adjustable Rampart, Funk, swivel knife with reworked blade.*

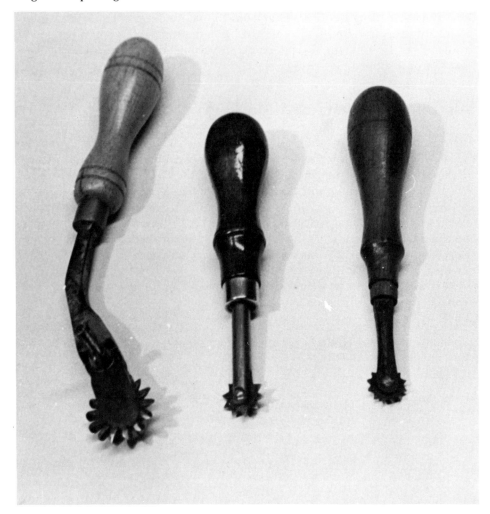

Stitching markers. Left to right: *#4 Dixon, #5 Osborne, #6 Osborne.*

I find that these work well for medium and large points, but not for the smaller points. There's a little tool that comes with a haft that loosens and tightens the chuck. A Tandy haft seems to work well with all awl points. You can't miss it—it's the only one they carry.

Sometimes the chucks loosen up in wood handles. I've found that the new space-age adhesives work well to tighten them up. Eastman 110 keeps all handles tight.

The old-fashioned awl hafts are very good. They're merely wooden handles with a little hole to start the awl down into. Inexpensive.

There are saddler's and harnessmaker's awl points. They're shaped somewhat like a broadsword. Harnessmaker's points work best for me. I keep a large assortment of blades and needles in a tight metal can. They rest on cotton impregnated with WD–40. Incidentally, I use WD–40 to fight rust on all my tools. I keep the tools on a rack at the back of the bench and on shelves. Rather than spraying them individually, I spray a light mist of WD–40 over them every week or so, right where they're kept.

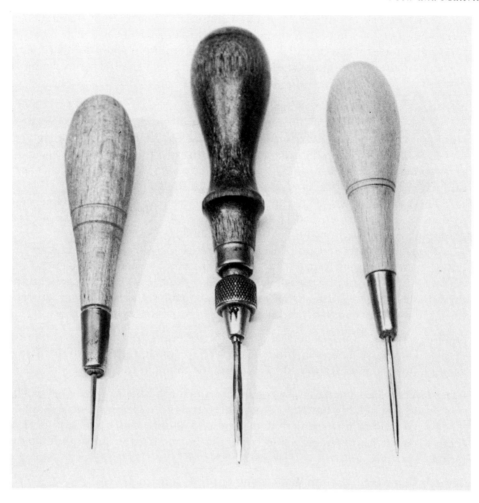

Sewing awls. Left to right: *small point, Tandy broad point, medium point.*

When you do enormous amounts of hand stitching, your awl point must suit you perfectly. No point works for me when new. If it's too thick, it's hard to push through the leather. If it's too narrow, it slips right through the leather, leaving a slit too tight for the needle and thread. So I first carefully narrow new awl points on my sander-grinder.

As I narrow an awl point, I test it on a piece of leather in my stitching horse. I may think I have the point just right—but it won't suit me when I test it. Back to the grinder.

When the awl point is just right, I pull it through a piece of emery cloth, eradicating the microscopic sideways grooves put on by the grinder. Final polishing comes from hours of hand stitching.

I baby my awl point when I have it just right. Not long ago I broke my favorite point and had the whole process to go through again until I got another one to suit me.

Another system is to have two awls and points. One can be cut down very thin and used to make a series of easy holes. Then the other awl, a thicker one, can enlarge the holes. Though this is double work, it's easier than fighting thick leather with the thick awl point.

Please excuse my interjections but I must say a word about maintenance. Keep your tools up where they should be rather than all over the bench. This will keep your shop organized. And it's a vital safety precaution—these tools are *sharp*. If you accidentally rest your hand on a razor-sharp knife, you'll seriously injure yourself.

Needles Needles for hand stitching come in various sizes: 00–0–1–2–3. I like a #2 for most saddle work. Unlike needles for sewing cloth, harness needles have blunt points. There is a groove on each side of the needle's eye. The saddlemaker makes "waxed ends" by pulling out part of the thread—thinning and tapering the ends—and laying it in the grooves along the needle's eye. If the thread hasn't been thinned enough, it'll stick as it's pulled through the leather.

There are various types of thread available. I keep an assortment of linen and nylon thread on hand. For saddle work I prefer waxed nylon. It's very strong and oil doesn't rot it. Put in right, it should last the life of the saddle.

To make a waxed end, pull the ends of the thread over a cake of beeswax a few times. Twist the thread to make it round; thread onto the needle. The linen I use isn't waxed, so I must pull the whole thread over the beeswax. The wax helps the thread wear longer and helps lock the stitches. You get needles from Osborne through most any company and most of these companies also sell beeswax.

Saddler's Pliers These pliers are used for squeezing parts of the saddle together. They leave a mark line that is followed for stitching. You'll find old ones around, but as far as I know, they're not made today in the U.S.A.

Glass Pliers These make a very good substitute for saddler's pliers. They can be purchased through big hardware stores, glass stores, etc. Brookstone sells them. They need a bit of reworking. Smooth the jaws so they won't mar leather. Use them to pinch leather together to cover the horn, stirrups, and cantle of the saddle. They are a *must have*.

Scratch Compass Used to mark along borders, horn hole, etc.

Compass Groover Osborne sells a compass tool that can scratch and groove. It features interchangeable points. I also have a compass-groover I got from the Joseph Dixon Tool Co., England.

Scratch Awls Handy to mark leather. Heavier ones are used to drive through the leather into the tree; for starting screws, stretching leather.

Strap End Cutters These come in oval and strap end (pointed). Used for ends of latigos, etc.

Steel Yardstick Used as a straightedge and measuring device.

Wood and Bone Rubbers and Folders Used for rubbing edges, pushing leather down in such places as under horn and under Cheyenne roll. Good ones are handmade.

Round and Oval Punches To make holes in leather. A full set is nice to have. For instance, the #1 is just the right size to punch the holes for Blevins stirrup buckles.

You should never hit your punches with a steel hammer. Osborne has rawhide mallets of various weights that are fine for this.

Poundo Board If you use a poundo board under the leather when you punch your holes, you'll keep your tools sharp. Tandy sells them. I put mine on a log that I keep on the cement floor.

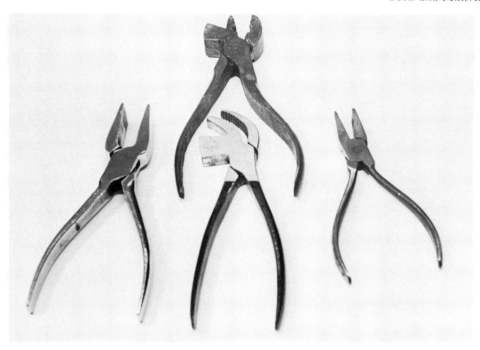

Saddler's pliers. Left to right: *glass pliers, pliers for stretching leather, utility pliers.*

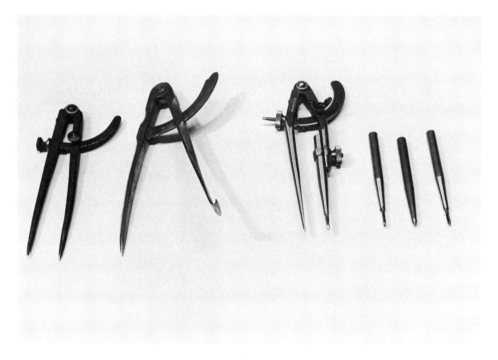

Compasses. Left to right: *scratch compass, English groover compass, Osborne scratch compass-groover, extra points.*

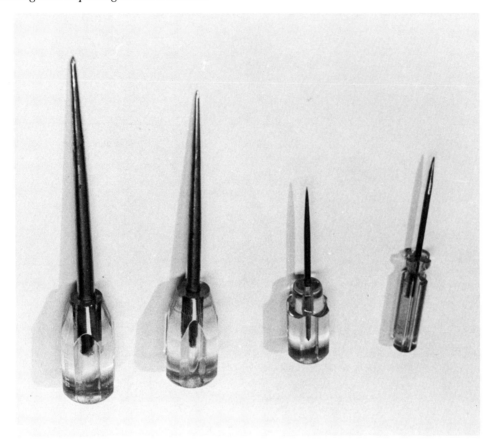

Scratch awls.

Small Anvil　Useful for riveting. Anything over 25 pounds is too heavy to be lifted up on the bench all the time. I got mine from a hardware store. It weighs about 10 pounds.

Riveting Tool　For riveting copper rivets and burrs. You rivet the stirrup straps to the fenders and secure Blevins buckles with rivets. You put rigging in the skirts with rivets. They come in various sizes but the #9 fits through the rigging plates and the Blevins buckles. Get them to fit the size rivet you use.

Rivet Cutter　Small, tough, sharp cutters that allow you to snip off too-long rivet ends. The new compound leverage cutters are fine for this.

Drawknife　Used for cutting straps. They're adjustable. A must-have tool.

Stitching Horse　Used to hold leather for stitching. This is a must-have. Every once in a while, someone starts making them for sale. You can keep abreast of such matters by subscribing to *Make It With Leather*, a bi-monthly magazine.

　　Check the detailed pictures of my stitching horse. Any good woodworker could make one for you. A band saw is needed to cut out the jaws. The seat needs to be made comfortable; you'll sit on it a lot. A radial arm saw can dish it out, as can chisels.

Deep Stitching Horse　We have all wanted deep throat stitching horses that clamp large leather pieces all the way from the top of the jaw to the stool. B.P.

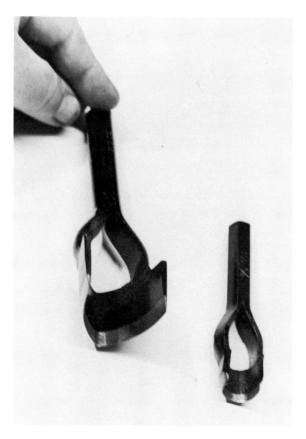

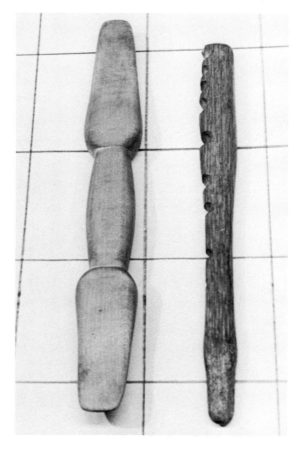

Left: Pointed-strap end cutter. Right: half-round cutter for pinking.

Homemade rub sticks.

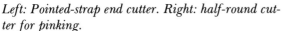

Marshall is making them. His primary business is that of Goldsmith-Silversmith-Engraver and I hear he's one of the best.

Alan Dewey, my friend, saddlemaker, and horseman, is also making them. They are hands and shoulders above a regular stitching horse. Alan is also producing some fine stamps for leather tooling.

Campbell-Bosworth Machinery Co. is buying stitching horses from both of these men and will have them in stock as long as there's a demand for them.

I have a homemade deep-jawed horse that's just the ticket for most saddle stitching. You can get a complete skirt in it. Anyone can make one of these.

Spokeshave Used for shaving down leather around the horn and cantle top before the binding's put on. This spokeshave has wooden handles that must be cut off to give clearance when working around the saddle horn. It is called Beechwood Spokeshave. I called the manufacturer and asked if these spokeshaves would continue to be available. They said that they would always have them, that the spokeshave was made especially for them. Other models are fine for shaping the seat.

Lip Knife This knife has a blunt point and is used where you must cut and shape leather as it rests on the final product. It keeps you from scarring leather with a knife point. Available from shoemakers or shoe-repair supply houses.

Various Hammers

Round and oval punches.

Leather Rougheners   Used to roughen leather before glueing. Available from shoemakers' supply houses.

Rawhide Mallets and Mauls   Used for stamping, punching holes, etc. Got mine from Colo Craft.

Skife   A small curved-blade skiving knife that is excellent for delicate work. Uses injector blades. Photo page 3.

Pinkers   Half round punches. Used for decorative pinking of leather edges— under the fork, say.

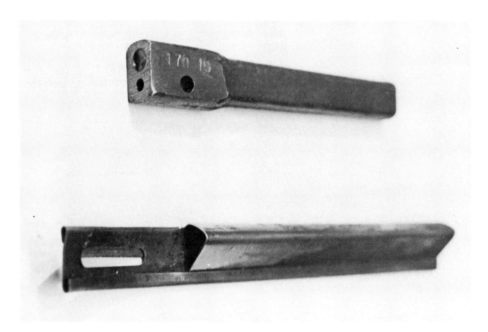

Top: *rivet tool.* Bottom: *skife.*

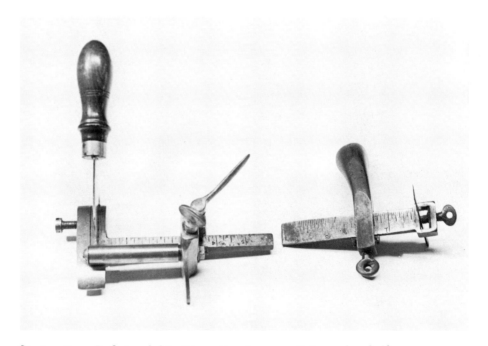

Strap cutters. Left to right: *Dixon plough gauge, Osborne drawknife.*

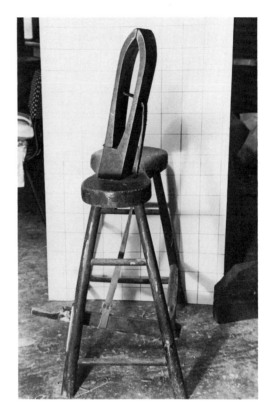

Stitching horse. Compute dimensions using grid at three inches to the square. This horse suits a small or average size man. Fasten the jaws under the seat using a peg and hole.

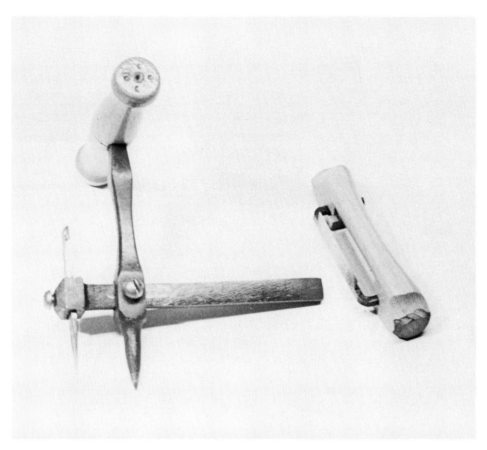

Left: *English washer cutter.* Cutter: *wood-handled spokeshave.*

Leather Smasher

Shears For trimming woolskin. I use sheep shears but most any good heavy-duty shears will work fine.

Leather Splitters This is an expensive tool. Keep your eyes peeled for good used ones at leather shops, flea markets, etc. Check horse magazines for folks advertising leather tools for sale. They can usually steer you onto one. Osborne makes a couple of good ones.

The leather splitter cuts down latigo, lace, and other thick parts. When making bridles, breast collars, halters, reins, etc., the leather should be split to a uniform thickness. Running leather through a very sharp splitter polishes the flesh side and improves the looks of the finished product.

Electric Drill This is a handy tool for the saddle shop. I drill most of my rivet holes with mine. Most punches make a beveled hole. By using an electric drill, you can make the hole the same size as the rivet. This makes for better and stronger riveting—the rivets don't fall out before you're ready to work on them.

You can drill out old rivets for repair. Most folks use a drill for this. It may scorch the leather.

Top: *rawhide maul.* Bottom: *Concha cutters.*

Miniature Power Tools   A better method of taking out old rivets is to grind off the burr part with a miniature grinder. A special cutting burr is used. They're a lot like a dentist's drill only larger. Mine has a variable-speed foot control. This doesn't get the leather hot. There are plenty of other uses for this tool in the leather shop. I bought mine, a Foredom, from U.S. General Supply.

Tack Lifter   You nail when you fit; then you have to pull the tacks out. The best tack lifters come from such places as Osborne. Theirs is a saddler's tack lifter.

Leather roughener.

Leather smasher.

Leather splitter.

Screwdrivers I use my electric drill for a lot of my screwdriving work. It's a half-inch, variable-speed machine, which is also reversible. I also have a very handy ratchet screwdriver, purchased from Brookstone.

Concha Cutters You can buy leather and metal conchas very cheaply from Standard Saddle Tree Co. But having your own cutters is a big help. Cutting conchas by hand is very tedious and it's almost impossible to do as good a job by hand as with a regular cutter. I bought a pair of used cutters from a Montana saddlemaker. You'll have to ask around for this tool. See photo page 16.

Handy Hardware-store Tools
  Vise
  Pliers of all kinds
  Rasps
  Nail Sets — Used to drive down nails in various places where you have no room to use the full face of a hammer.
  Metal Punch — For punching holes in galvanized metal. We use D-rings under leather conchas and the hole punch makes the screw hole for this.

Stamping and Carving Tools We don't go into leather tooling in this book. There wouldn't be room to do a complete job of it and there are many books available on the subject.

Pattern Paper You make patterns for the parts of the saddle. Most of these patterns are made oversized. You cut the leather out according to your patterns and then cut it down as you make the saddle. You have to vary some of the patterns for different saddles. Most of the patterns can be made from the heavy brown paper your leather comes wrapped in. Or you can buy good paper from artist and office-supply houses. Poster paper is fine.

Glue Pot   Almost all the saddlery supply houses carry glue pots. A good pot makes working with glue much easier—and you sure will have to do a lot of glueing.

Contact Glue   Barge is the best I know of. They even have a quick-drying kind. You cement both pieces of leather. When dry, place the parts together. Make sure you've put them in the right place—they won't come apart.

Jack Carroll (Carroll Saddle Co.) says that they use epoxy for glueing leather together, and that it won't come loose when the saddle's oiled. I like Barge better and find that you'd have to use a heck of a lot of oil to make it loosen up. Almost all leather supply houses sell Barge cement. You can also get it from shoe-repair places.

Dexterine   This is a dextrose glue. You just add water to it and it's ready to use. Very messy. It's used on the parts of the saddle that are glued down but that have to be worked after glueing. I put this stuff under the fork cover, cantle binding, etc. I put it on the horn wraps and it makes the horn very hard.

Oxalic Acid   Mix it with water. If you get leather dirty, clean it up with oxalic acid. A must. Tandy sells it. Colo Craft sells it. Most other companies sell it.

Edge Finishers and Polishers   Gum tragacanth is a fine product for edge finishing. You moisten the leather edges, apply gum, let it dry a bit, and then rub with stick or canvas. Binds the fibers of the leather.

Tragacanth comes from Iran and is expensive. A pound of it cost me $80. However, it'll last me many years. I bought it through my drugstore. When I was checking this out for my book, I called Tragacanth Importers, Inc., in NYC. They say they have a product that will do everything gum Tragacanth will do. It is *much* cheaper. I believe Colo Craft will sell some to you. The product is called Ticaloid 2–10–A. You can rub edges with a rub stick, a light piece of canvas, or brown paper from a sack. All work well.

Fiebing Co. makes all manner of dyes and edge coatings. They also have a gum tragacanth solution that works much better than what you can make up yourself—a homemade solution isn't stable, and will soon spoil.

When using dye and gum, moisten the leather's edges, apply and rub smooth with a tool handle, light canvas, or brown sack paper. Felt and wool dye daubers are available from Tandy stores.

Another fine way to rub edges is to use glycerine saddle soap and rub it into your canvas. Rub paraffin into a canvas to polish edges of latigo. Rub only one way.

Pure Neatsfoot Oil   We oil saddles as we make them, for there are parts the horse owner can't oil after the saddle's completed. We don't recommend regular oiling as saddle care. Products like Farnam's Leather New, Horseman's One Step Conditioner and Cleaner, Leather Balm, and, of course, a good saddle soap all clean and condition saddle leather. It's a good plan to lightly saddle soap the leather before you cut it from the side.

Garbage Bags   These are good for casing leather. Most leather parts should be soaked in water and cased for a while before using. Cased leather cuts better, works better, and molds better. Don't put leather in a plastic sack and forget about it—it'll mold. If you do get mold in a bag, throw it away and use a new bag.

Tacks, Nails, Screws, Rivets, Thread   All can be obtained from Standard Saddle Tree Co. You can get your brass escutcheon pins from them. These are used under the fork when you secure the fork cover. They make cinches. You can get stirrup buckles, stirrups, and all the other things you'll need from them. They have a catalog and will be happy to send one to you.

Saddler's Stamp   When you decide to start your own saddle shop, you'll want a saddler's stamp that names you as the maker. I got mine from H.T.S. Corp./14701 Keswick St./Van Nuys, CA 91405.

Leather   Leather can be obtained from tanneries and leather companies. A few companies have ads in the latest *Western Horseman*. Buying from a company is more expensive than buying from a tannery. With the latter, you usually have minimum orders, usually a roll—which consists of ten sides. Sholze Tannery will sell individual sides but charges about a 20% mark up. Or, rather, they give you 20% off if you buy a roll. There is lightweight, medium, and heavy skirting. The medium is about $^{12}/_{14}$ ounce. The heavier is usually $^{13}/_{15}$ ounce. I usually buy heavyweight. More about this later.

Saddle Tree   You'll need to order a custom tree. I'd suggest ordering a catalog and checking out the different styles. The company will want to know the length of seat, gullet height, gullet width, cantle type, cantle height, horn type, and tree width. The regular western tree has a $5^1/_2$-inch gullet width. The semi-quarter horse has a 6-inch gullet width. The regular quarter horse tree has a $6^1/_2$-inch gullet width, and the wide quarter horse tree has a $6^1/_2$-inch gullet width and a wide flare to the bars. The regular gullet height is 8 inches, while the gullet height for high withered horses is 9 inches. The Standard Saddle Tree Co. catalog is very detailed in explanation and they delight in helping all aspiring saddlemakers get just what they want.

About 40 people work at Standard Saddle Tree Company and produce some 15 thousand saddle trees a year. They work the saddlemaker to produce what the customer wants. During my saddlemaking years, I've talked directly to the president of the company, Lawrence Fox. Mr. Fox recently retired and A. Packard Condie bought the company, which will continue on as before.

A softwood pine is used for the trees. There has to be a certain amount of give to a tree and soft wood works best. The tree's strength comes from the bullhide covering.

LeGrande Hadlock is the master tree maker at Standard and is one of the best in the business. He's been at it for over 30 years.

Special templates are made for a design. A saw cuts out the tree from rough wood. After the templates and wood are in position, the saw operator simply checks for mistakes.

The rough-cut tree parts are rasped smooth and fitted together. The metal saddle horns are then bolted clear through the tree. A mixture of gauging and fiber hardwall is applied, which fills the bolt and nail holes and makes a smooth hard finish over the horn and tree.

After the hardwall has dried out, the tree is taken to the sewing room, where the wet rawhide is sewn onto it. Rawhide lacing is used to sew it together. It takes over an hour to sew the wet rawhide in place. The stitches are pounded down with a pneumatic hammer.

After the rawhide has dried out, the tree is checked to make sure it's not out of alignment. Then it's pounded again. It's put in a drier for three days at 93°. The final step is to apply a coat of special varnish.

When I talk to a customer, I want to know his height, weight, in-seam, and what use the saddle will be put to. If the customer is a roper, he may want a straight front tree with a dally post horn. A post horn sits right straight up—like a post.

Saddler's stamp.

He'll want the tree a little longer than usual since he'll want to move back a little to give himself room to dally (take turns of the lariat around the horn).

The bronc rider or horse breaker will sometimes have to ride bucking horses. If he uses a straight front tree with a post horn, he'll get hit in the stomach or chest when he leans forward to get with the bucking horse. He'll want a shorter tree. If he uses a long tree, he'll be thrown back against the cantle, and he'll blow his stirrups.

Figuring out an order for a customer, I'll tell Standard Saddle Tree Company that I want a 15-inch seat, a 4-inch regular cantle that is 13 inches wide, a 14-inch fork width, a small #1 horn, an 8-inch (regular) gullet height and semi-quarter horse bars on an Ellensburg tree. This order might be for a fellow from 5'9'' to 6'4'', medium to stocky build, who will be riding colts and broncs. If the horses had high withers, I'd order a gullet height of 9 inches rather than the regular 8 inches.

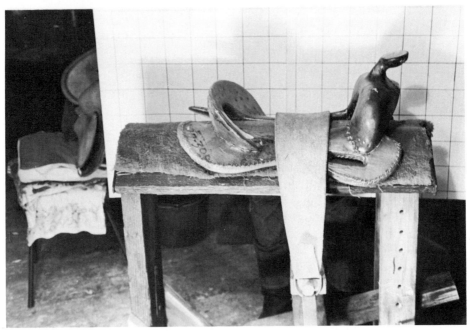

Draw-down stand. Compute dimensions using grid at three inches to the square.

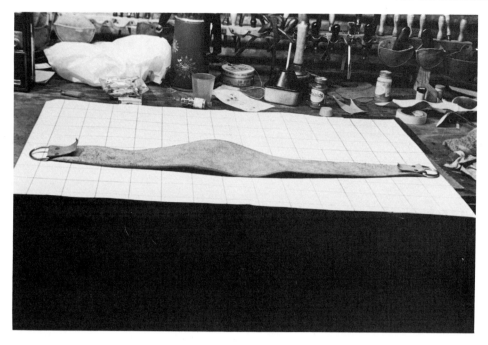

Draw-down strap.

When in doubt, the tree company will help you with your problems. It's best to call and ask for help.

Sheepskin, Latigos, Saddle Strings You'll need two sides of skirting leather, latigos, lace for the saddle strings, and a large jumbo sheepskin. You can get all this from a tannery or a leather company, such as Tandy. Make sure you get bark-tanned sheepskin. The chrome-tanned doesn't work too well for saddles.

If you're just making a saddle or two, buy your latigos and strings already cut. If you plan on making quite a few, buy $^5/_7$-ounce latigo for lace and $^9/_{11}$-ounce for saddle latigos.

Draw-Down Stand Before you start building your saddle, you must build a draw-down stand. They're easy enough to build. It serves as a stand while you're working on the saddle and it's a must when you shape the seat. Cut a draw-down strap to fit over the seat. Use a lever to draw the strap down tight to shape the damp-cased seat, and dry the seat out to shape on the draw-down stand.

2

Step-by-Step Saddlemaking

Starting the Saddle

It's a good idea to have a good old saddle on hand to check yourself with. If the saddle isn't being used, take it apart piece by piece to see how it was made. You can always put it back together again. It might be made differently from the one I'll build; note the variations and put that knowledge to good use.

Hand Stitching

Hand stitching is basic. It's the way saddles and harness were put together before sewing machines were invented. Hand stitching is much slower than machine stitching—but as good or better. Even if you do have a machine, there are parts of the saddle that have to be hand stitched. You need to do it well.

First case the leather—dip it in water and put it in a plastic sack, so that the moisture will work all the way through the leather. If you soak a fender or stirrup strap for ten seconds and immediately put it in the bag, this will be enough to condition the leather. You can control the amount of moisture absorbed by the leather by soaking it for a longer or shorter time, or by removing it from the bag and partially drying it out. After the initial soaking, you may dampen the leather with a sponge, if necessary.

MAKING A SADDLE

1. Saddle soap two sides of leather
2. Form patterns, cut out necessary parts
3. Cover the gullet
4. Put in the ground seat
5. Cover the horn
6. Cover the fork
7. Fit up the skirts
8. Fit up front rigging
9. Fit up back jockeys
10. Glue front rigging to skirt
11. Take skirts off saddle and rivet in rigging plates
12. Glue on sheepskin. Sew top and front sheepskin to skirts

25

13. Put skirts back on saddle and glue on back jockeys
14. Sew back jockeys to skirts
15. Fit up seat
16. Remove skirts
17. Fit up cantle filler and cantle back
18. Sew on cantle binding or Cheyenne roll
19. Oil skirts, fenders, stirrup straps, and attach
20. Attach skirts to tree with screws
21. Put on conchas, latigo holder, saddle strings, and stirrups

Figure out how far you want the stitching to be from the edge of the leather piece. Set the stitching groover accordingly, and groove the leather. See photo on bottom.

Next, to ensure that your stitching is uniform, run a stitching marker along the track made by the groover. The most common sizes of markers are the #5, #6, and #7; these sizes reflect the number of marks per inch put down by the tool. See photo at top right.

There are various kinds of thread used by saddlemakers. In this country the most common kinds are linen and nylon. We mostly use waxed nylon—it's very strong. I get mine from Standard Saddle Tree Company.

The thread ends must be tapered to make them small enough to go through the eye of the needle. Thinning the thread is called making a "waxed end." To make a waxed end, hold a fairly dull knife at an angle away from you, and pull the thread under the blade, removing some of the thread. Make two or three passes to get the thread thin and beveled.

Using a stitching groover.

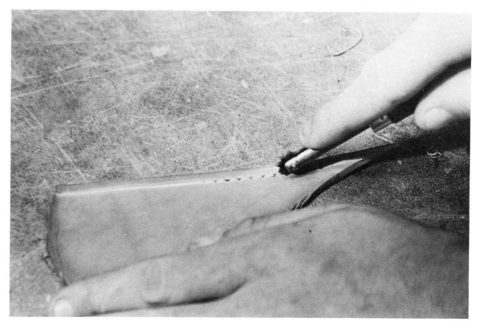

Use a stitching marker in the groove you cut out. This will ensure that your stitching is uniform.

Pull thread ends under a knife blade to thin and taper them.

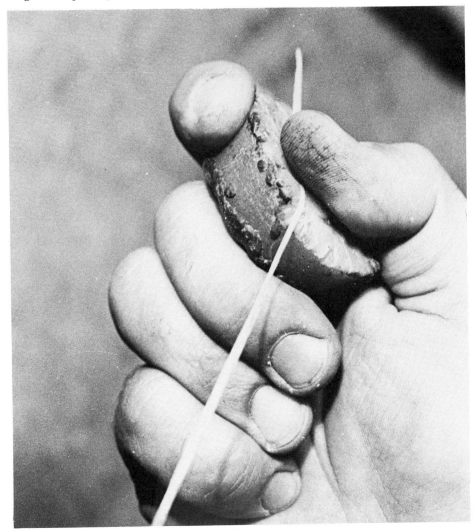

Pull the thinned thread ends over a cake of beeswax.

Twist the ends of the thread into points. The thinning process will have removed the wax from the thread ends, so pull them over a cake of beeswax. If you're using unwaxed thread, wax the entire length. Roll the waxed ends over your leg to round them out.

If you tear the thread from the needle as you sew, you've thinned the thread too much. If the lump where the thread passed over the eye of the needle pulls as you push it through the awl hole, you've not thinned the thread enough. After a week or so, you'll be making waxed ends like an old pro. Don't be discouraged if you don't do too well at first.

Now thread the needle. To do this, first pierce the thread with the point of the needle about two inches from the end of the thread. With the needle remaining in the thread, pierce the thread again ⅛ inch from the first pierce. Make a third pierce. Pull the pierced thread up to the eye of the needle; thread the needle. Pull the thread snug, and pull the pierced thread over the eye. Now the needle's fixed

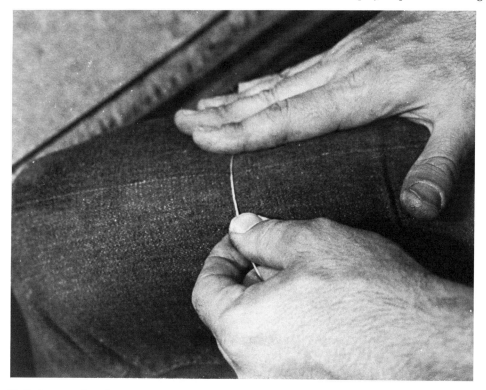

Roll the waxed ends over your leg to round them out.

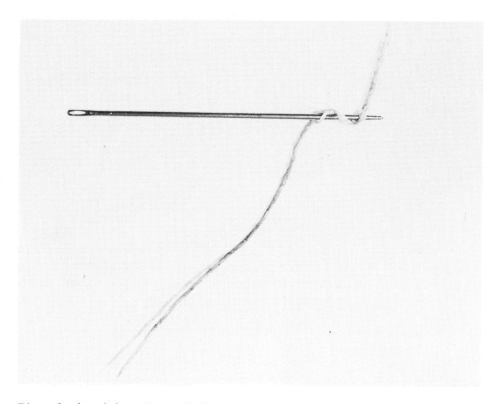

Pierce the thread three times with the point of the needle.

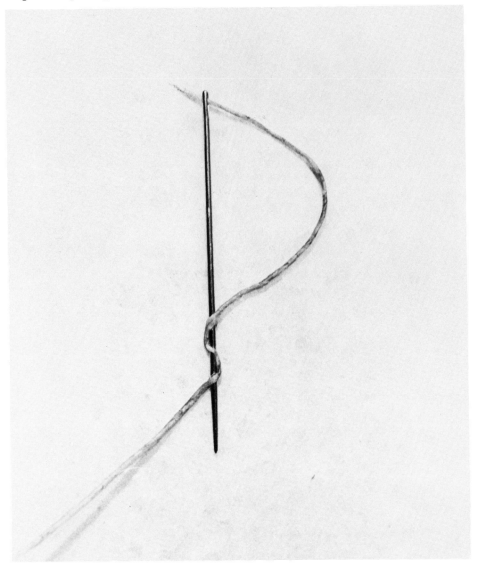

Pull the pierced thread up to the eye of the needle; thread needle.

to the thread, and once you repeat this operation at the other end of the thread, you'll be ready to sew.

To sew, take a needle in either hand. Pick up an awl with your right hand and punch a hole through the leather at the stitch mark. Make the hole at a 45° angle to the stitch line. You do this because the awl point is shaped something like a broadsword and if you punched holes parallel to the work, one after another, the distance between the stitches would be narrowed too much. You might tear out the leather between the holes when you pulled the thread. This would ruin the work. My English friend Kevin Truselle tells me that English leather workers take great pride in being able to put in as many as ten stitches to the inch without weakening the leather. If you figure sewing parallel to the work as 0°, awl holes punched flat with the work line would be at 0°. The holes punched with the blade held straight up would be 90°. So you punch the holes exactly at 45°.

Pull pierced thread over threaded eye, pull snug, and you're ready to sew.

Now start away and sew toward yourself, following this procedure:

Push a needle through the hole and get both ends of the thread exactly even.

Punch another hole, using your free hand to support the leather against the awl. With practice the awl will slip between, rather than through, the fingers, though we all wound ourselves occasionally.

Now pass the left needle through the awl hole. Pick it up with your right hand and pull the thread out about six inches. Hold this first thread out of the way as you push the right-hand needle through the same hole—in front of the first

Punch a 45° angle hole with the awl.

First pass the left-hand needle through the awl hole. Pull the thread out six inches.

thread. Pull the first thread to the left to make sure the second needle hasn't pierced it. Cross the first thread over the second needle.

Pull threads snug. Then grasp both threads, so that they run over the little fingers. Pull tight. This is hard on the fingers, so guards should be worn. You'll

Push the right-hand needle through the awl hole. Test to see that the first thread isn't pierced. Then cross the left-hand thread over the needle.

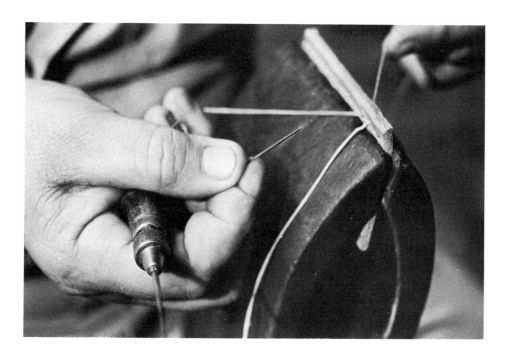

Pull both threads taut with your little fingers.

build up calluses after a while, but you can still cut through the calluses on occasion. If that nylon thread slips, it'll cut you. To protect yourself, cut the fingers off old leather work gloves; overstitch the machine stitching so it won't unravel. Or

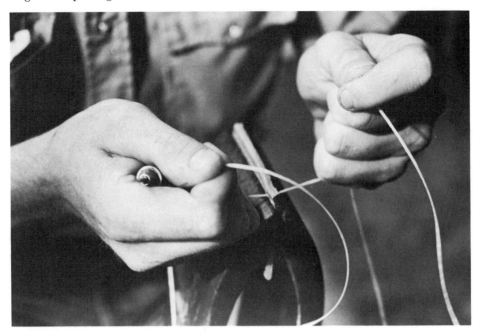

Threads are pulled uniformly every stitch. To do this, you'll probably need guards for your little fingers until calluses form.

Square knot.

make your own guards from light garment leather. Soak this leather in water and do some stitching so the wet guards will shape to your fingers as they dry out.

Learn to pull thread in a uniform manner; if there is even one loose stitch, the work will never look uniform.

Continue sewing until stitching is completed. When finished, take an extra turn around the second needle with the first thread while pulling it back. This is called a lock stitch. In fact, you may turn the thread around the needle each stitch, to make a tighter bond. However, don't count on a lock stitch to hold the end of your stitching. Sew back over the end of the work at least two stitches—lock stitch each one. Then cut the ends off right at the leather. It'll hold.

When sewing short pieces, it's not necessary to make new waxed ends each time you finish a short line. Punch two awl holes. Start in the one nearest you. Run your threads through the hole and leave them about 4 inches from the end. Tie both ends in a square knot above the work; pull up snug. Sew the hole away from you and come back over your stitches. You're then hooked up and sewing again. Done correctly, it's hard to tell this from the other stitching. When finished, cut the thread with the square knot off at the stitches.

You don't need to use the square knot when starting with the two pieces; there are places where this isn't possible. Just leave an inch or so of thread sticking out of the first awl hole. Sew away and then back over the first stitch. After the second stitch is in, pull tight the two threads that stick out.

When the stitching has been completed, roll an overstitch wheel over the stitches. This helps to make the work a little more uniform. Try it once and see if you like the results.

Finally, use an edge beveler to round the edges of the leather. Polish the edges.

Cutting Leather

To make a neat saddle, you have to do a good job of cutting the leather.

Make the patterns from the paper the leather was wrapped in. Make the patterns oversized, or allow a bit when using them. Such parts as the seat, fork

If necessary, use an overstitch wheel to even out your stitching.

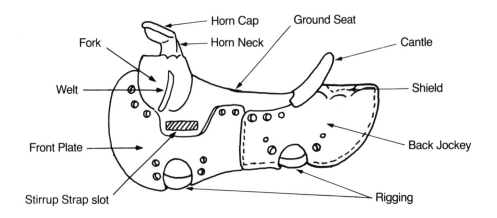

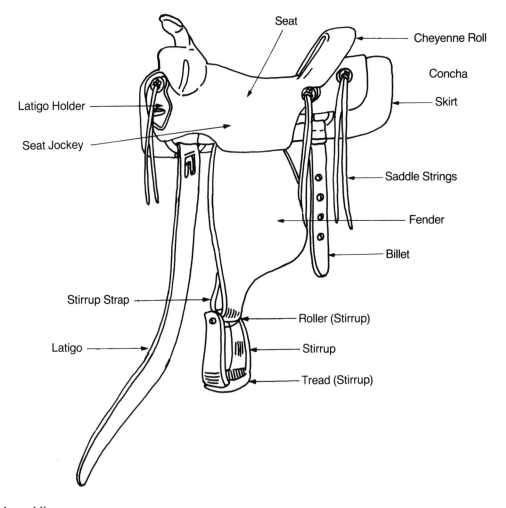

Parts of the saddle.

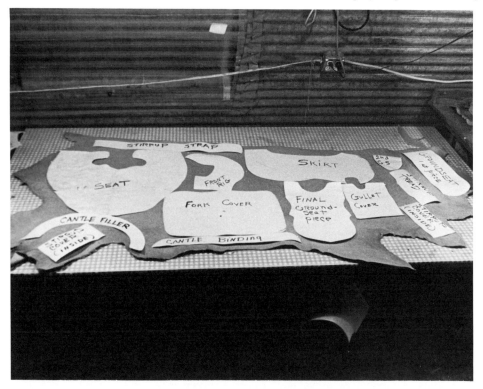

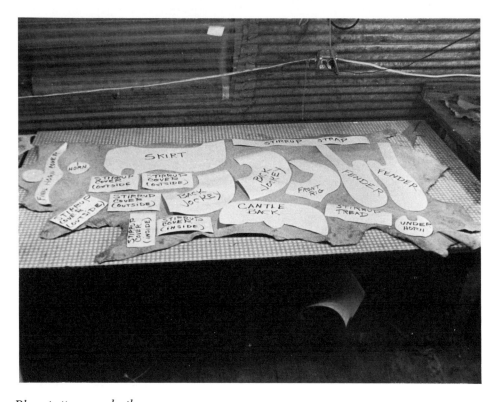

Place patterns on leather.

cover, gullet, horn cover, and back jockeys should be cut oversized. Cut fenders, stirrup straps, billets, and back cinch to the exact size.

Have the leather cased—moistened—as described on page 25.

Set the leather on the cutting board—a grainless board is best. Maple cutting blocks can be purchased. Masonite (pressed wood) makes a fair cutting surface. Both sides can be used but the rough side is best. The knives chew it up but a 2′ x 4′ Masonite board should last six months. I keep a piece of this on my workbench. High-density polyethelyne is very good, though expensive. I have a sheet of this standing by that I use for precise cutting. The knife should go just through the leather and slide over the poly surface. Cutting too deep is hard on the poly surface and on knives. You can break the points by cutting too deeply.

Place the patterns on the leather.

Mark the leather around the pattern with a scratch awl.

Push the point of a round knife through the leather to make the cut. Be sure that the knife is very sharp.

The small round knives with sharp points are the best for cutting around curves. You need to be able to get the handle down low for curve cutting. Osborn's large knife is very good.

Take care to hold the knife straight when cutting. You can be so concerned with cutting on the line that the blade gets tipped at an angle. Practice!

Round knives are also used for skiving—thinning the leather. For instance, the edges of the gullet cover are skived very thin, as are the wings of the horn wrap.

Skive on marble or glass to keep the knife from catching on the cutting surface. Heavy glass is excellent for this purpose.

To skive, hold the knife very flat. Have the knife very sharp and the leather thoroughly cased. Stop every few minutes and strop the knife. Practice on scrap leather until you gain proficiency.

The little Osborne "skife" is a very good tool for delicate skiving.

Hold knife straight when cutting leather.

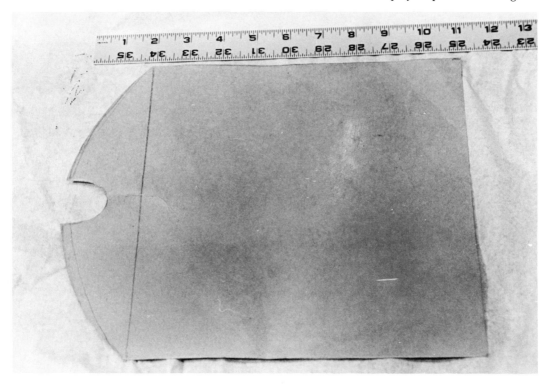

Gullet cover.

Tack the gullet cover in place.

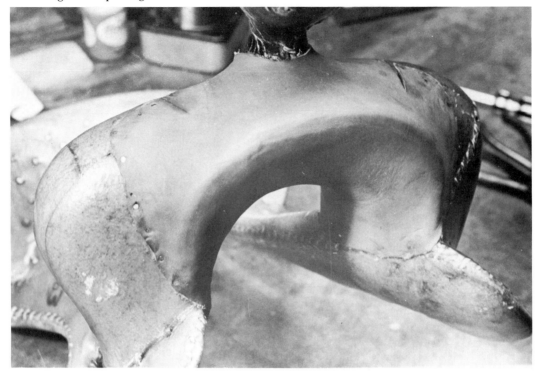

Finished gullet cover.

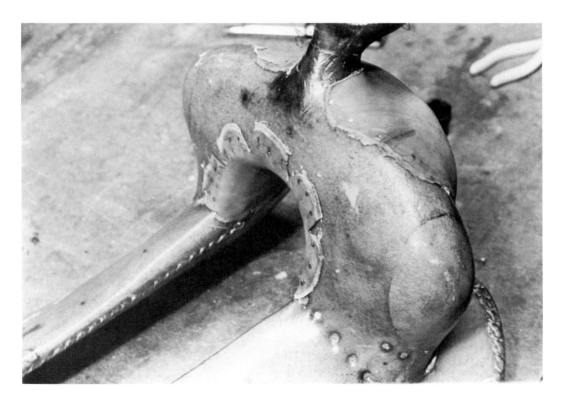

Back view finished gullet cover.

French edgers are very useful for skiving. I have a complete set that runs from 1/8th inch up to 5/8th inches. They're pushed up as you'd push a chisel. Mine come from the Joseph Dixon Tool Co. of England. **AT LONG LAST**, they're available in this country from:

> Mike Schiller Leather Machinery Corp.
> 718 N. Flagler Drive
> Ft. Lauderdale, Fla. 33304
> phone outside Fla.   800-327-9420
> in Fla.   305-463-7918

Covering the Gullet

There is no practical reason to cover the gullet. You do this for looks. It's done first because you can't get at the gullet later. And it's a good thing to start with, as it's fairly simple to do.

My gullet pattern is 9 inches by 11 inches. Remember, most patterns are extra large. Cut the leather for this from the belly. It must stretch quite a bit when it's put in. Case the leather well, and skive all edges thin. After fitting, the gullet cover is reskived before it is finally put in place.

The back of the gullet fastens at the base of the fork. Tack this in place. Mold the gullet cover with your hands, so that it covers part of the bars. It can be fastened at the front lip of the fork or brought up higher around the horn. I prefer the latter method.

Stretch the gullet cover as much as possible and tack in place. Don't seat the tacks; you're just checking the fit. The gullet cover should extend from the place where the bars meet the fork—in back—under the fork and then up over the edge of the fork. Mark excess spots with the scratch awl. Take the cover off and cut it down to fit. You'll probably have to skive the edges again.

Check the gullet carefully. If there are lace seams or rough places, you may wish to fill with saddle paste (Dexterine). Those rough spots will show up when the leather dries.

LEATHER PARTS OF THE SADDLE

Underside of gullet	Cantle binding
Ground seat pieces, at least three	Seat
Horn cover—3 pieces	Stirrup leathers—two
Skirts—two pieces	Fenders—two
Back jockeys—two pieces	Leather covering for stirrups—
Front rigging leathers	4 inside, 4 outside
Fork cover	Stirrup tread
Cantle filler	Stirrup chafe
Cantle back	

Put the Dexterine on the gullet cover and tack it down. This paste will hold the top line in place, so that you may eventually pull the tacks out. Dexterine really dries slowly but it makes a hard bond. When the cased leather has dried out, the Dexterine will also be dry. If some of it oozes out from under the cover, wipe the excess off with a damp sponge or rag.

Putting in the Ground Seat

There are several ways to put in ground seats. You can use a one- or two-piece galvanized-metal (24-gauge) strainer. You can cut your own or buy them from Standard Saddle Tree Company. The metal ground seat is all right if put in correctly—the part you sit on must be very low and flat.

There is a plastic ground seat available but I've never used one.

And there is the all-leather ground seat. In my opinion, this is the best.

When I first witnessed a saddlemaker in action, he used the metal ground seat. Jack Link and I were breaking horses near Cripple Creek, Colorado. He needed a saddle so he made a deal with Jack Schwab, owner of the Cottage Inn. Schwab would buy the material for two saddles and Jack would get his saddle for making Schwab's. The trees were purchased from Harry Rowell and were about as perfect as trees could be.

Jack was a fine saddlemaker and soon had them finished. He showed me quite a bit about it and taught me to hand stitch. This was my first real taste of saddle work—back in 1949.

Some years later I decided to make my own saddles because I couldn't buy exactly what I wanted. They were just plain work saddles and I didn't pay much attention to finishing. But these plain saddles rode like they had built-in rocks. About that time, Bruce Grant's book *How To Make Cowboy Horse Gear* came out and the back of this book had a section on saddle making by Lee M. Rice. In it, he explained the all-leather ground seat. I tried using one and the difference was fantastic.

MAKING AN ALL-LEATHER GROUND SEAT

1. Cut a strip of heavy neck leather one inch wider than the slot between the tree bars, and some four inches longer than the slot. If you care to, put garment leather under this first ground seat piece.
2. Skive edges thin, tapering back one inch. Taper the front, leaving heavy leather at top front. Skive the back down fairly thin.
3. Tack down the leather, making the back taut by pulling and tacking from side to side. Offset the leather to the right just a bit and pull to the left to get it centered. Don't bother stretching the front too tight.
4. Put tree on the drawdown stand. Place handmade front shaper under the front of the ground seat. Attach drawdown strap over the back of the seat. Push drawdown bar down. Take some time to allow the cased leather to stretch before securing the bar. Work at this until you have the front pushed up where you want it. Remember that the leather is slow to stretch. Give it time. You can come back every five minutes or so and get a little more stretch out of it if you want it. You are actually making an arch form—the strongest architecture known to man. Let it dry.
5. Second ground seat piece.
6. Seat plugs.
7. Final ground seat piece.

8. Plastic wood to reinforce the seat at the front sides. When the plastic wood has thoroughly hardened, varnish it.
9. Garment leather.

Now, the all-leather ground seat takes longer to put in than the metal ground seat because you have to let the first piece dry out thoroughly before proceeding. However, you could be covering stirrups or something like that while you waited and it shouldn't really hold you up.

Everyone works out his own method of doing things. I work with level-ride saddles so my methods differ slightly from Lee's.

First, cut a piece of heaviest neck leather so that it laps over the slot in the seat about one inch on each side and back. Skive the edges thin. The heaviest leather goes to the front. The rough or flesh side of the leather goes up.

Mark the center of the ground seat with a soft pencil or felt-tipped marker. Then find the center of the tree. Put a mark at the base of the horn and another at the center of the cantle so you can always keep things centered.

You're going to stretch to the left, so place the first ground seat piece a little to the right of center. Put in a couple of #14 saddler's tacks just in front of the cantle. Take a heavy scratch awl, drive it through the leather opposite your first tacks. Offset the awl, so that it'll stretch the leather. Tap the awl through the rawhide into the tree. When the leather has been stretched a bit, tack it down. Now you have four tacks in place and the back of the ground seat should be centered. Pay close attention as you stretch—the skived leather may tear. It takes a bit of practice to know just how far you can safely stretch the leather. If you do tear the leather, readjust the seat and start over.

Next, anchor the front of the ground seat an inch or so above the bars of the fork. Anchor up and out. A galvanized 1½-inch nail is OK for this. Bend the nail, which, as it bends, will stretch the leather. This action will pull the seat a bit

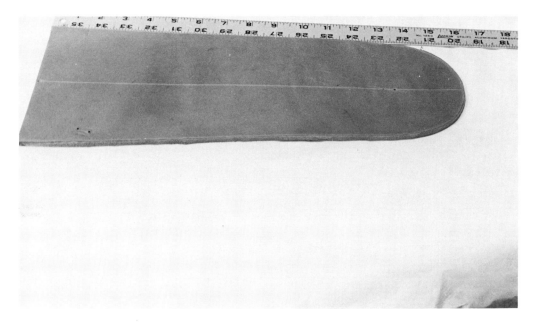

First ground-seat piece.

Skive the first ground-seat piece.

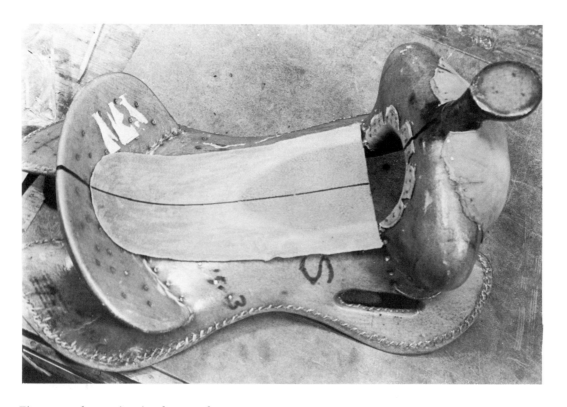

First ground-seat piece in place on the tree.

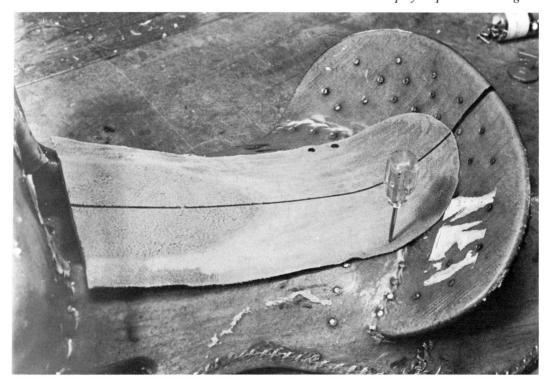

Use an awl to stretch the first ground-seat piece into proper position.

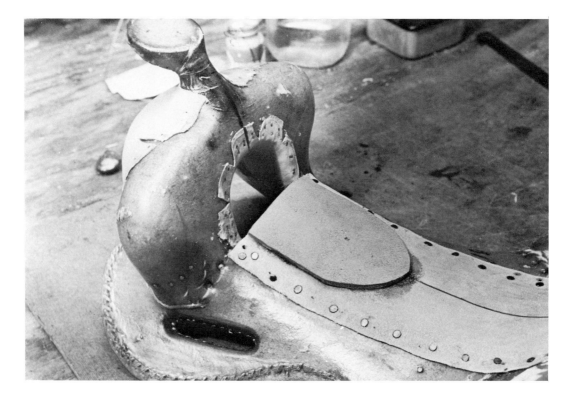

Second ground-seat piece in place on the tree.

off-center. Do the same on the other side of the seat. This should stretch the leather back into position.

Carefully use your scratch awl to pull the leather at the sides down onto the tree. Tack in place, stretching the leather down. Work on one side, then on the other side at first. When you become proficient, you'll be able to tack one side down completely and then move to the other and it'll all come out all right. When you've finished, cut away the excess leather where the bars meet the fork. Pull out your anchor nails on the fork.

The second ground seat piece follows the contour of the bars. It's a triangular piece, skived thin at the edges. This piece narrows the seat between the rider's thighs. If the person you're making the saddle for has thick thighs, add a third piece to narrow the seat down still further.

When I put the second ground seat piece in, I cut the leather to size but don't skive the edges. I roughen the leather so contact cement will get a good hold, and glue it on dry so the cement will hold better. After a piece is glued down (flesh side—rough side up), I moisten the top with a sponge and cut it to fit the contour of the saddle. Skiving the edges down when you have the work glued in place is, for me, more precise than skiving on the bench.

Cut the last ground seat piece full. It covers the whole seat. Again, the harder, thicker part goes to the front. If the back—where the rider sits—feels a little thick, skive it down. The back of the seat should be very flat. Put this piece on wet.

You can put this last piece on a couple of different ways. Tack it down where it should go, let it dry out, remove it, and contact cement the whole thing down. Or you can use Dexterine and nail it right down. I prefer the latter method since Dexterine helps make the ground seat very hard and will help it always hold shape.

Second ground-seat piece after skiving.

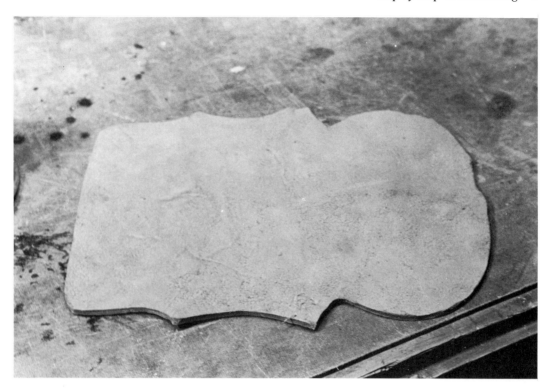

Final ground-seat piece.

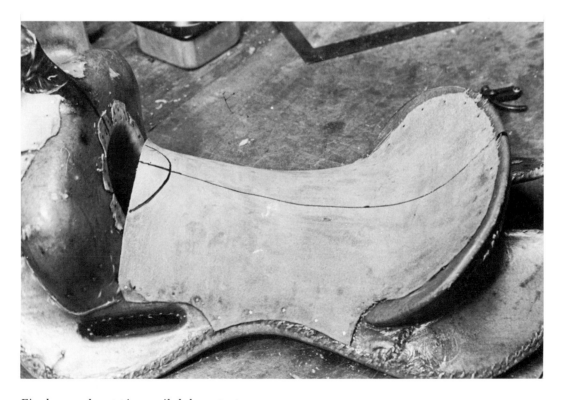

Final ground-seat piece nailed down to stay.

When a pro saddlemaker reads this, he'll say I forgot something. That something is the garment leather or light chap leather that is always put down first (almost always).

A year or so ago I was building three saddles at once and put garment leather on before the first ground seat pieces. As I looked at the trees on the bench, I thought the back of the seats looked a little high. So I removed the garment leather. The ground seat pieces looked better that way. After the ground seats were completed, I cut the garment leather to fit and glued it down. I'm sure it'll hold up as long. Of course, the bottom of the ground seat should be roughened before contact cementing it to the garment leather.

Before the garment leather goes on, the handhold must be cut out. Use your scratch compass. Figure out a point about a third of the way up the horn. Set the other compass point at the junction of tree bar and fork. Scratch a light line and check it to make sure it suits you. If it does, scratch heavier and cut out all the leather on that mark. Use an edger and leather knife to bevel the handhold edges.

When you cut the garment leather to fit the slot under the ground seat, cut it at least 1 inch extra large. The garment leather will extend up over the handhold part of the ground seat and onto the front of the ground seat. Apply contact cement to the flesh side of the garment leather. Scratch the leather you're covering. Apply cement. Where the garment leather goes on the top front of the ground seat, you'll have to cut three or four slits to get the leather to pull down snugly. Pull each piece of this top garment leather with a pair of pliers. Rub smooth with a rub stick.

If we've ever really had complaints, they've been over the front of the ground seat on level-ride saddles. The regular tree is built with a riser that raises up the front. You have to build over that riser. It raises the front of the ground seat

Wedge used to raise the front of the ground seat.

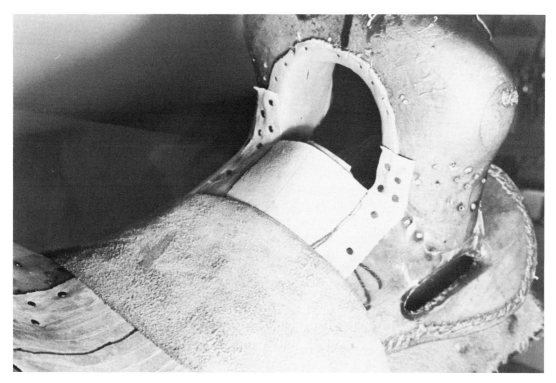

Wedge in place under ground seat.

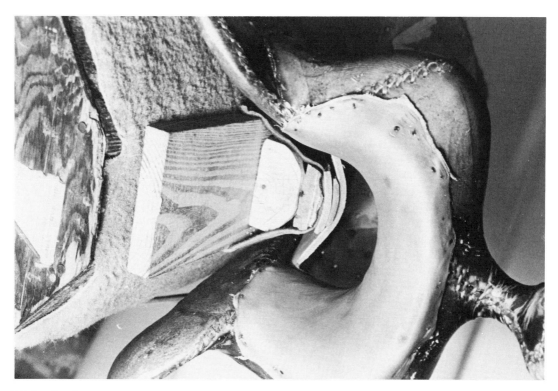

Wedge in place.

enough that it shouldn't hit the back of the withers on a high-withered horse. Trouble is, to narrow the front you have to build up the seat front pretty high and this makes for a drastic slope back to the cantle. Most western saddles have this slope back.

We have cut away the leather on the bottom of the front of the ground seat. This works, gives adequate clearance. However, it might weaken the ground seat so I tried to devise a better plan.

I made a sloping rounded piece of wood that is shaped like a horse's withers. My first ground seat piece isn't stretched much at the front. The leather is very well-cased. I put the tree on the drawdown stand, cinch it down tight with the seat strap, and tap this piece of wood under the front of the ground seat. The leather will *slowly stretch*. Tap the wood a little bit more every few minutes until you have the front raised enough to do the job. Raising the center of the ground seat front an inch is plenty. Let it dry out thoroughly. It might narrow the front enough that the second triangular piece isn't needed.

The next step will be the final ground seat piece. Put it in with lots of Dexterine. When dry, the whole seat will be very hard and firm. The glue sandwiches the two pieces into a firm bond—like making plywood. It makes the whole seat much stronger.

I asked Lee Rice about this. He said that he'd had the same problem when low-roping saddles became the vogue. To solve the problem, he anchored the center of the ground seat up on the middle of the fork and let it dry out. After his ground seat was finished, he applied plastic wood between the bars and the leather on each side of the front of the ground seat for greater strength. When this was dry, he shellacked over the plastic wood. He said that this made a very firm seat that lasts the life of the saddle.

If you use a metal ground seat, you must put garment leather down first. It would be best, on a level-ride saddle, to use a two-piece metal ground seat. One piece is flat and covers the back of the seat. The next piece overlaps the first, so fit and trim with metal shears before nailing down.

When the last ground seat piece is in place, search out any lumps or bumps. Look for them and feel for them with your fingers. Smooth them out with a spokeshave or skife. Do a good job on this for it's the difference between an excellent and a poor saddle.

Before I started making saddles for sale, a couple of saddlemakers wanted to make saddles I designed. The last company I tried made a saddle for me on a tree I sent them. The workmanship was nice but the saddle didn't ride very well. In fact, none of my riders wanted to use it. Since it was a regular rather than a quarter horse tree, we had use for it on narrow horses.

One day I decided to check out the ground seat in this saddle. I took the seat off and went after the ground seat. There was that galvanized metal. I'd been promised that an all-leather ground seat would be used.

I put the leather ground seat in that saddle, replaced the seat and put it all together. Then the saddle was placed in the tack room. I didn't tell anyone I'd reworked it.

Next day, I told one of the riders to use that saddle. After his ride, he said, "You know, I think a saddle just takes a little getting used to. I had a real good ride and like that saddle a lot."

In the out-of-print book *Saddlemaking*, by John H. Beck, he describes two pieces of leather he uses when putting in the metal ground seat. These are called "seat plugs." They go on each side of the ground seat at the back just in front of the cantle and are used to make a broad, flat seat. They're put in before the final

Ground seat with optional plugs.

ground seat piece. I think that this is an excellent idea as it's a way to eliminate the "riding a log" effect.

I wanted to get permission to mention John H. Beck's method in this book, so I called him. He's a fine friendly man and he gave me some good advice. When he worked for Porter's, they used "seat plugs" a lot.

Mr. Beck advises me that he doesn't always use seat plugs. This depends upon the tree. Some trees already have a broad, flat seat built into them. The trees with a rounded seat need them.

When you fit the metal ground seat, the slot in the strainer must correspond to the stirrup-strap indentations in the tree. The leather that covers the slots must be cut away sometimes. There's no real reason to do so before fitting the seat.

But, perhaps, you might want to put the stirrup straps and fenders on the tree to get an idea how everything looks when you're fitting up the seat. The leather over the slots must be cut away to do so. Make some awl holes at the corners of the slots to get a line. Carefully cut out the leather. Save this leather! You need to tack it in place when you shape the wet seat on the drawdown horse.

One more thought before moving on. This concerns the all-leather ground seat. Due to the shape of some cantles, care must be taken to get the first piece down flat in the back. On a dished cantle, this center part might hoove up as it dries out. Leave tacking it down until last. If it appears to want to hoove up, press it down before nailing. It's more important to keep it flat than to stretch it drum taut.

A sandbag can be used to hold down the back of the ground seat and the seat as they're drying. Mine is made from an old pair of jeans. I sew one end closed, add sand until the leg is pretty full, then sew the other end closed.

The three leather pieces needed to cover the horn.

Tack the leather circle into the horn top.

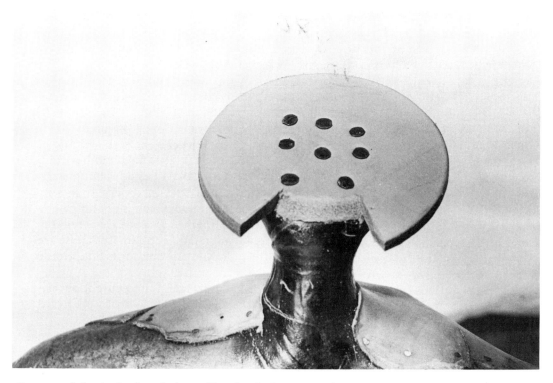

Cut a notch in the leather circle to allow for the horn-cap wings.

When you push this piece down, you'll notice how it flattens out. If you're really working with a lot of dish in the cantle, it might be wise to lay some Dexterine along the sides of the back of the slit and tack the ground seat down as close to the slit as possible. The glue will hold it down—draw the whole back down as it dries out. A lot of this depends upon the tree you're using.

Covering the Horn

There are several ways to cover a horn. I'll describe one of the most common methods. It's always used to cover large horns and can also be used to cover the smaller horns.

First, cut out a heavy stiff leather circle. Cut it at least an inch wider all around than the horn. If you're covering a 3-inch horn, cut a 5-inch disk. You don't need to soak it. Rough up the top of the horn but don't cut into the hide.

Find the exact center of the horn. Make a hole there by tapping a heavy-duty scratch awl with your hammer. Find the center of the leather disk and punch a small hole in it.

Put contact cement on the roughened horn top and on the piece of leather. When the cement is dry, drive a tack through the centered hole in the leather and into the awl hole in the horn. With the leather centered, press the leather down to get a firm bond. Now drive four or five tacks through the leather into the horse. This will keep the horn cover from loosening up.

Make a pattern for the cover. Then find some leather that will give you a fairly stiff horn cap with flanky wings (see photo p. 52). Cut the bottom of the horn cover from very flanky leather—especially if you're covering a Mexican-type horn—for it must stretch a lot when put in place.

Dip the wings in water but try to keep the horn top dry. Skive the wings very thin—they must stretch. The horn top should be about the size of the first piece you put on.

Cut a notch out of the circle you've tacked on the horn. The notch should coincide with the leather that joins the top and the wings.

Roughen the top piece already secured on the horn. Apply contact cement to this piece and to the horn-top cover. Don't get any cement on the wings. When the cement is dry, glue the top in place.

Roughen the bottom of the horn. The bottom cover can be put on dry if it's flanky enough. If not, wet the grain side. Apply contact cement to the bottom of the horn and the bottom of the horn cover. Glue in place. Rub the bottom part up to the top with a rub stick. Rub out any wrinkles. Turn the tree upside-down on the bench to do this.

You'll have the tree upside-down on the bench many times. Since it's easy to nick or mar the horn, take care to protect it: Place an old piece of carpet on the bench, or make a protective cap for the horn out of scrap sheepskin. Both ways are good. The more uncoordinated you are, the more you need to protect the saddle you're working on. I'm very uncoordinated.

With the horn-cover top glued in place, the next step is to secure it permanently by stitching. You need to know *where* to stitch. Now you'll see why your glass pliers are one of your most valuable tools.

When I got my glass pliers, I filed down the grooves on the jaws—these might mar the leather. The pliers then had a smooth bite. Dampen the leather on the horn cover, so that the pliers will leave a definite mark. Crimp along the edge of the horn. Take your time. Before long, a definite line will appear.

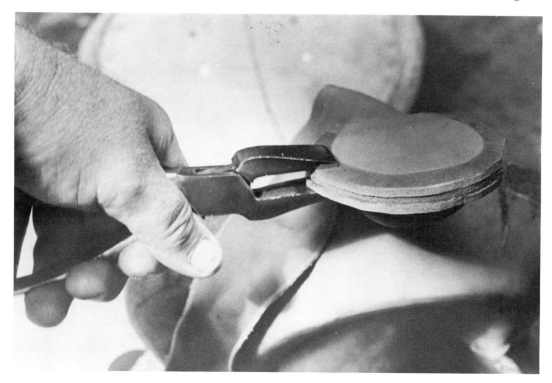

Use pliers to mark stitching line on horn top.

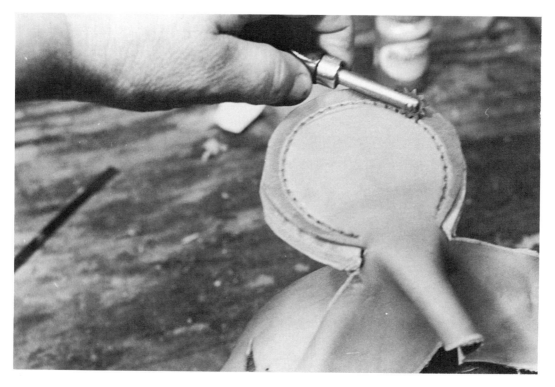

Mark a stitch line on the horn top with a stitch marker.

Sew the horn cover.

Chinaman in use, pulling the leather around the neck of the horn.

Check the line on the bottom of the horn cover. Rub in a good line with your rub stick. You can use a pencil on this line to make it more distinct. Your sewing awl must come out on this line.

Take your saddler's compass and scribe a line $1/16$ inch from the plier mark on the horn cover. This will give you a perfect circle to stitch around.

Cut a groove on the top line with the swivel-knife blade or a freehand groove. Then use a #5 or #6 stitch marker to make stitch marks down in the groove.

Sew the horn cover. Take time to punch the holes evenly and make sure the awl comes out splitting the underside line. Hold the awl straight up and down. Punch every hole the same say. Remember to punch at a 45° angle. Pull the thread very snug and pull it the same way each time.

The wings should be very wet. Usually the right wing is pulled first. It's pulled tight around the horn and tacked lightly in place in back of the fork. You pull, rub with your hands, rub with the stick, etc. Rub out all the wrinkles. The leather will slowly give and stretch. As you take out the slack, pull the tack and set it again as you progress.

You should have a "Chinaman" for the second (left) wing. This is a long piece of latigo. It gets better with use so make it out of good stuff. The end of the "Chinaman" has a loop in it that has been tripled and stitched. (You use a spike in this loop for leverage when pulling the wing into place.) It is 30-inches long, $1^3/4$-inches wide at the loop end, tapering to 1 inch at the narrow end. It is doubled back 3 inches. The hole for the spike is $1^3/4$-inches long and $7/8$-inch wide.

Put the left wing in place. Shape and pull it by hand until you have it shaped as much as possible. Watch that the leather doesn't tear when you pull it. Give it time to stretch. Wrap the Chinaman around the horn. Leave the end sticking out a little

Smooth the edge of the horn with a wood spokeshave.

so you can hold onto it. Put your spike in the slot of the Chinaman and lever it to pull the Chinaman very tight. Leave it in place as the leather sets. Then check it for wrinkles and uneven places. Rub everything smooth. You can stop now, tack it down and call it finished.

Or, to make a very hard horn cover, use Dexterine under the last wrap. Loosen the last wrap, apply Dexterine, and pull the wrap back into place. You can leave the Chinaman in place as the Dexterine dries. If the Chinaman leaves any ridges, dampen the horn and rub them out later.

A word of caution. Latigo leather has been dyed and this dye will come off on your horn cover. It's a good policy to saddle soap with wet suds quite a few times before putting the Chinaman to use. If any dye does come off on the horn cover, clean it up immediately with oxalic acid.

There are other methods of covering the horn. One method is to cover the horn cap and then use a wrap with a half top cover as the final step. This is often used on smaller horns. Other methods—rawhide edge, latigo edge, etc.—aren't too difficult.

To finish the horn cover, compass a line out from your stitching a little more than ⅛ inch. Cut on this line with a leather knife or round knife. You can round off the edges with an edge beveler or a reworked spokeshave, which will do a better job. I got my wooden spokeshave from Woodcraft Supply Corp.

When the edges are smoothly rounded, apply gum or saddle soap and rub with a hammer handle, canvas, brown paper, etc., until smooth and glossy.

Covering the Fork

When Jack Link was making the saddle for the saloon owner, he ruined the fork cover. This brought on some mighty cussing since Jack hadn't ordered any surplus leather. But wasting leather didn't bother him as much as making a silly mistake: He made his original cut too small. When he worked the leather around to where it should go, it didn't reach the bars on each side of the fork.

I have a fork cover hanging in my shop to remind me to be careful. I cut too large a horn hole and it looked bad.

Some really top saddlemakers can make a fork cover that goes on a swell fork saddle without sewing in a welt. Ed Hughes owned about 150 horses and we had them at the ranch where Jack Link and I were living. We contracted to break a good many broncs and Ed furnished committee saddles (R.C.A. approved) for us to use. Jack was amazed that the forks were covered like slick fork roping saddles—no welts. He often commented about this. I didn't see where it mattered a bit. I do now that I'm a saddlemaker.

To cover a fork, cut a piece of flanky leather about 16 x 22 inches. Find the center—that is where the horn hole goes. The heavier leather, the part toward the top of the back, goes to the front. Wet and case the leather thoroughly before using.

You have to get the cover on and off the fork several times before it's finished. A large horn hole is amateurish yet you must be able to get the cover on and off fairly easily. A large horn with a thin neck just can't be covered without cutting a slit back of the horn for room. Forcing a fork cover on by using great muscular strength usually means ripped leather. Any thin-necked horn that has a cap size over three inches needs this slit. Of course, it helps to pink all the way around the hole, but that isn't done a lot today.

Fork cover in place.

Measure the base of the horn where the hole will rest when it's in place. Cut the hole about two-thirds the size of this measurement. I use a washer cutter to cut the hole (hardware-store item). Bevel the edge of the hole. Gum or saddle soap and rub to a gloss. If the horn cover can't be forced into place, cut a slit down the back. Take great care to get this cut centered exactly.

Covering a Slick Fork

First, we'll look at the job on a slick fork—one without welts.

After the cover has been slipped over the horn, mold it out from the horn on both sides. Push the leather flat, stroke it over and over to mold it snugly over the tree. Make sure you keep the horn hole centered.

Set an inch-long box nail at the rim of the fork—the front, where the fork joins the bar. Nail it a half inch or so from the front meeting place and nail it into the bar. Do the same on the other side.

We'll make a folded-under front. Scratch a line along the front rim of the fork on the side that doesn't show. At the front, where the fork meets the bar, make a hole with your sewing awl. Do so on both sides. The scratch line should meet both holes.

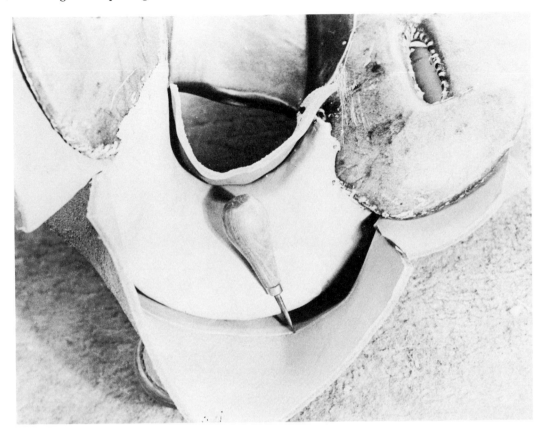

Scratching a front line.

Move to the back. Work some leather toward the center so that the leather bulges out a little more than ½ inch from the fork at the center. Set a nail in the bar on each side of the hand hold. Make a hole with your awl on each side of the hand hold and cut straight back. You'll now be able to mold the leather at the hand hold under the gullet.

If there's a moderate amount of slack in the leather down by the bars, you can rub a lot of this out with your rub stick. If there's too much slack to do anything with, pull the front nails and work the slack to the front. Carefully working slack to the front is the way a rounded fork can be covered. When everything looks like it should, cut two slits out from your front awl holes. If you've pulled the front nails and pushed the leather to the front, you'll need to scratch a new line at the fork front.

Make a light scratch line along the rim at the back of the gullet. You already have a front scratch line. Remove the fork cover. Compass a line about a half inch past the scratch line. Use a half-round pinking punch along this line.

Now for the front scratch line. Compass a line about ⅛ inch out from your scratch line. This will be the fold line. Now scratch a sloping line ⅛ inch out about four inches long in the middle of the scratch line. Scratch a line about ⅛ inch back from the scratch line on both sides from the center. This is necessary for a correct fit over the front.

Now scratch a line about 1¼ inches out from this last line. Cut the excess leather off along this line; this is the part that will be folded under. Skive the edge

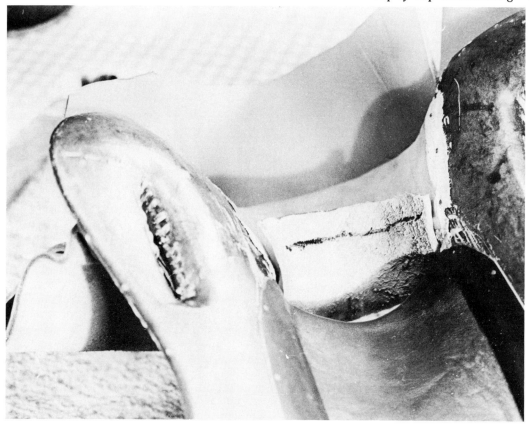

The dark horizontal line is what you should pink.

of this folded-under piece very thin.

Fold the leather back on your fold line and rub down. Put the fork cover on and check for fit. Then take the cover off, contact cement the folded-under piece down and/or sew it down.

When you check your fit, check to see how much leather is folded over the bars. It should lay over from ½ inch to an inch. Where the leather is too much over, scratch with your awl. Take the cover off the fork. Trim off the excess and skive the edges. You should now be ready to finish it up.

Put the cover back on the fork. Make sure the horn hole is centered. On a large horn, you'll have a slit in back of the horn. Make sure it's straight. If there's overlap, make a rounded cut in the back to take out the slack. At any rate, mark a line straight on down the middle of the fork. Take the cover off and check this line. If you've had to make a double cut to take out slack, both sides should meet exactly. You'll have to lace this slit, so punch lace holes now. I suggest "gaucho" lacing.

GAUCHO WEAVE

The Gaucho weave, used to lace up the back of the horn hole, is fairly easy. If you want the lacing to lay pretty flat, the lacing should be split thin and the lace holes should be farther apart than illustrated. But if the lace is

A fork cover that has been fitted and removed from the fork. Stitch lines are indicated.

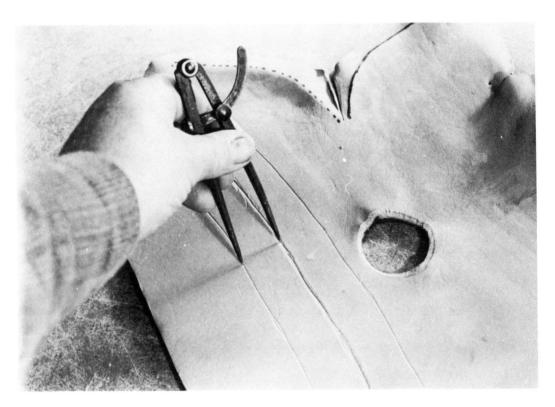

Compassing out the front to be rolled under.

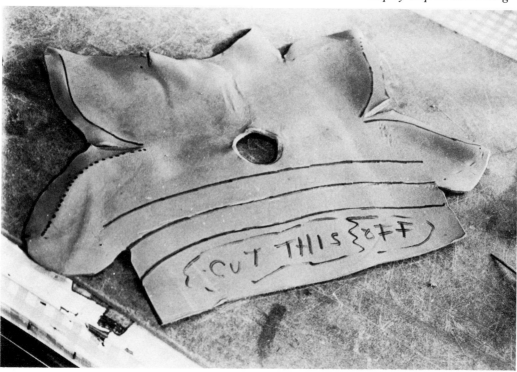

The compassed lines have been inked in for clarity.

too thin and the holes are too far apart, you may leave gaps that won't be covered. Practice on scrap leather until you get it to suit you.

For the lace itself, I'll cut a length of ⁴/₅-ounce lacing leather that I use for saddle strings. Indian tan is fine for this. Then I'll run the lace through the splitter to make it as thin as I need.

The lace should have its edges beveled so it'll lay flat. Bevel the rough side, not the grain side. To get a clean bevel, I soak up the lace and rub saddle soap into it.

I use a sharp knife to bevel with. I push the point of the knife into the worktable and hold my thumb against the blade so that thumb and blade make sort of a draw gauge. Then I pull the lace between my thumb and knife blade, so the edge is cut at a 45° angle. This sounds harder to do than it is. Practice until you get it right.

The lace holes should be fairly dry in order that they won't stretch out as the lace is pulled up snug. I may rewet the fork cover after the lacing's done if I need to have wet leather to stretch down the fork cover.

1. Push the leather lace through the top holes. Work from yourself toward the center. Feed the lace back to yourself through the same holes.
2. Push the right top lace through next lower hole to the left. Push the left lace through the opposite hole to the right.
3. Push the lace through the top hole again, from underneath. If you want a flexible job, push the left lace through the left hole. It isn't important to

Starting the gaucho weave.

have flexibility here, so the left lace is pushed through the top right hole and vice versa.

4. Push the top left lace under the second-hole lace.
5. Bring the top right lace to the third hole and pass it under lace that has just been used—the top-left.
6. The top left lace has been run through the third hole to the right. Now both laces come from underneath and run through the second hole. Repeat the process until the lacing is finished.
7. Lace across the bottom to finish the lace. Push the lace up through a few strands on the underside and cut off.

Lace up the slit. Now spread a saddle paste such as Dexterine over the fork.

Never use contact cement for this—you'll need to move the cover around quite a bit to get it just right. Dexterine takes a long time to dry out so there's no need to rush after you apply it. If excess paste oozes out, clean it up immediately with a damp sponge or rag.

Put the cover in place. If it doesn't want to come down to where it should be, set your spike to draw down and gradually, carefully, pull it down to where it should go. Keep the spike-hole low where the seat will cover it up. Your first drawdown with the spike should be at the junction of tree and bar—in the front.

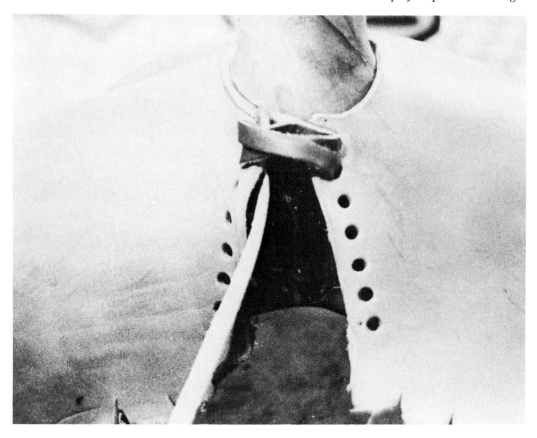

Bring the first string to the second hole, then return it through the first hole.

Draw down the other side. Make sure you haven't pulled the horn hole off center. Here's where you may have to adjust. Don't panic. It'll come. Drawing down with a spike will ensure that everything stays in place. Rub! Push with your hands. Set your final nails to draw the leather down. You can pull down a lot with nails. Nail all around the fork. Rub down any puckered-up leather on the folds over onto the bars.

Turn the saddle over and put brass escutcheon pins through the center of the pinked pieces of leather.

Covering a Swell Fork

Some fine saddlemakers work slack to the front on swell-fork saddles and manage to cover these forks without a welt. Not me.

You'll have a *lot* of slack to get rid of on a swell-fork saddle. Make sure you gather this slack evenly on both sides of the fork—uneven welts look peculiar. Cut off the slack about an inch from the fork. Now you need your glazier's pliers.

Crimp both sides of the slack, pulling the leather up snug around the swell. It sounds harder than it is. The pliers will leave definite marks to follow; simply cut the leather off at these marks, punch, and lace. You don't see as much of this today as you used to. Most saddlemakers sew in welts. When the slack has been pinched,

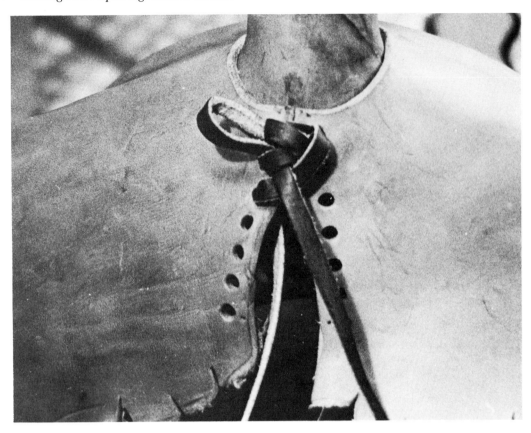

The weaving about to start.

take a knife and make a mark at the base of the fork on both sides. This ensures that you'll get them even at the bottom when you get ready to sew in the welt.

There are two kinds of welts—the single and the double, or folded, welt. In *Saddlemaking*, John Beck says that the double welt is the thing—that single welts are put in cheaper saddles. But his book was written in the fifties—today you'll see many fine saddles with the single welt. It's easier to put in and easier to describe, so I'll tackle it first.

Single Welts

Cut a couple of pieces of leather (welt fillers) ³/₄-inch wide by ten-inches long. Cut a slit in the end. Soak and case this leather.

With the fork cover on the tree, check the height of the cut. Cut as high as the loose slack you want to take out. When you use your pliers, you might not slit the fork cover high enough.

Turn the cover inside out. You should easily see your plier marks on the reverse side of the leather. Scratch a definite line so you can find it easily.

Jam the split in the strap tight into the top of the cut. Use slick box nails about a half-inch long and nail where you'll stitch to hold the leather in place. Line up both slits you made at the base of the fork. Pull the thread pretty tight as you sew and put in 6 or 7 stitches to the inch.

Completed gaucho weave.

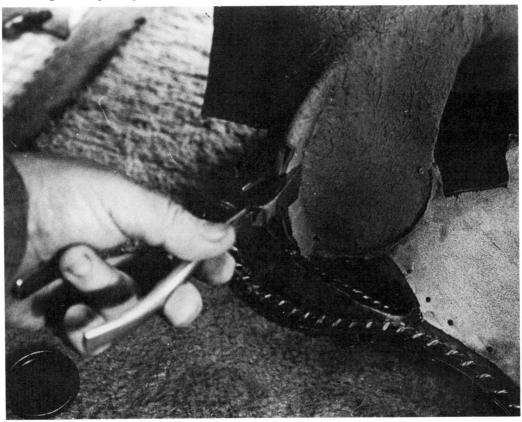

Use glazier's pliers to crimp a welt line.

Take a sharp knife and *carefully* cut the welt right down to where you can see the bumps made by the stitching. Leave a thin tab at the top. This tab will ensure that you don't have a gap at the top of the welt in the final product.

With welts sewn in place, turn your fork cover right side out. Take a tack hammer and pound the welt flat. Hold the fork cover loosely in your hand when you do this. When working with heavy leather, you'll have to pound pretty hard to get everything straightened out.

Check for fit. Put Dexterine on the fork and proceed to secure the cover with nails. Cut off excess outer welt with a French edger.

Double or Turned Welt

The double or turned welt is harder to put in—you need to be very meticulous getting the turned edge precisely in place. You have no excess leather to play with.

Latigo leather is used for many turned welts. Regular leather can be used but it must be thoroughly wetted or it will crack when you bend it. The double welt is turned back in on itself.

Cut a piece of latigo leather 10-inches long and 1½-inches wide. Skive down both sides. Glue the leather together so the doubled welt is now ¾-inch wide. Leave an unglued piece, skived thin, ½–¾-inch long for insurance so that you

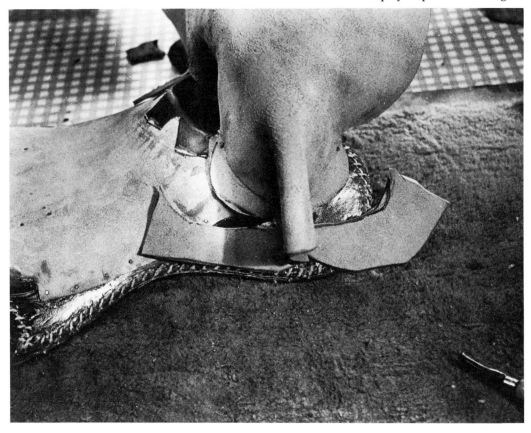

Excess leather where the welt will be.

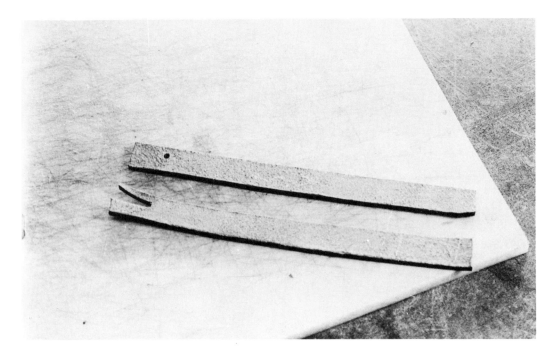

Welt fillers.

Pinking iron, mallet, and pinked back of fork cover.

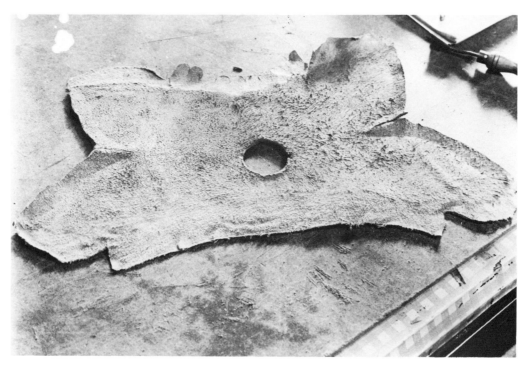

Fork cover ready to have welts sewn in.

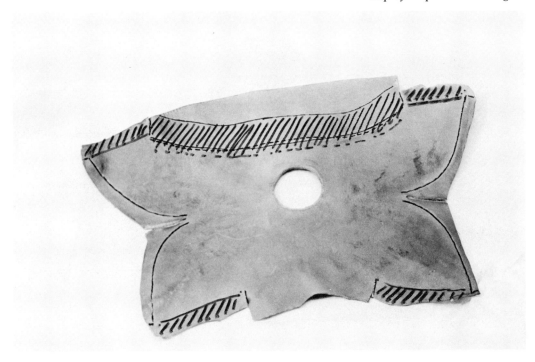

Shaded areas are to be skived. Front has not been trimmed in this photo.

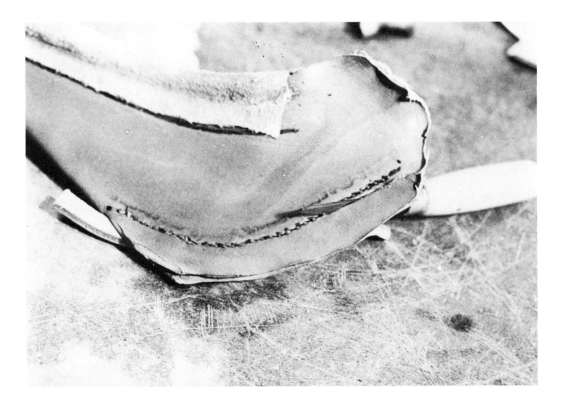

Welt has been stitched. All excess leather—right down to the stitches—is cut off.

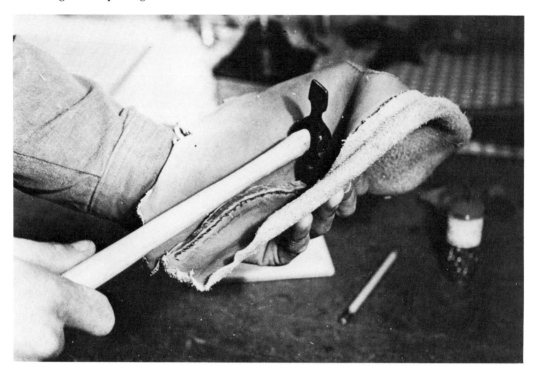

Reverse fork cover and pound welt flat with a tack hammer.

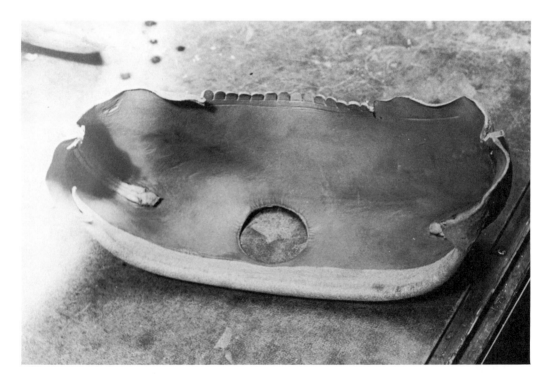

A reversed fork cover shows where welts are pounded down with a tack hammer.

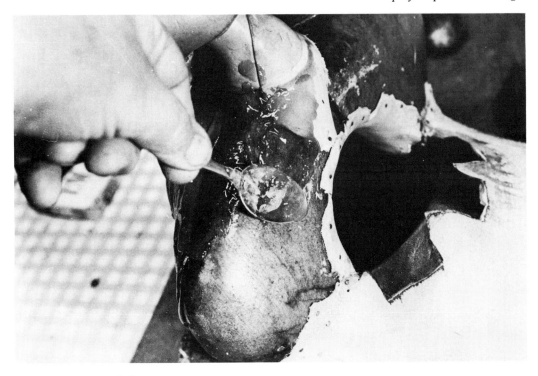

Apply dexterine to fork cover.

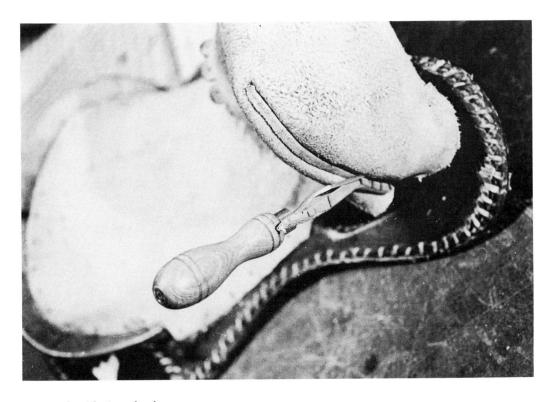

Trim welt with French edger.

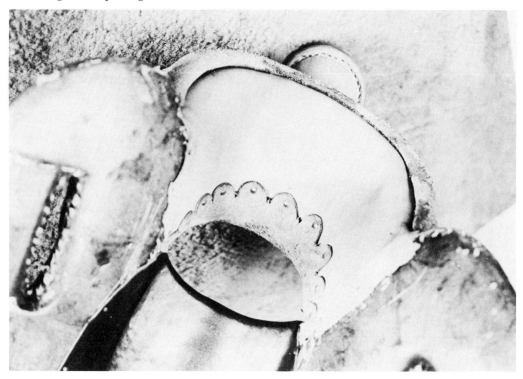

Ready to nail fork cover in place.

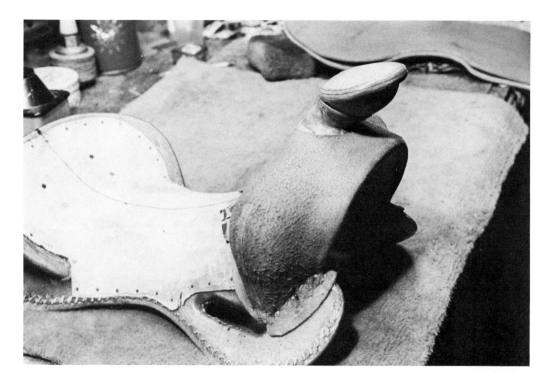

Finished fork cover.

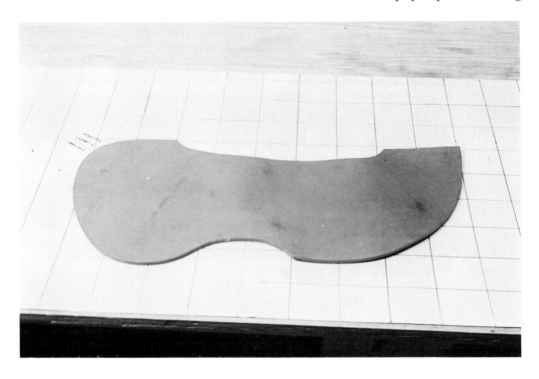

A skirt.

won't leave a gap at the top of the welt. Jam it tight into the cut leather. You have to line the doubled edge up *exactly* with your plier lines. Line up the cuts you've made at the base of the fork. Tack to hold for stitching. Finish the inside as per instructions given for the single welt.

Skirts

I make a pattern for the skirts or use an old pattern that's of good fit. To make a new pattern, I take a piece of heavy paper, lay it on the upturned saddle bar, and carefully draw a line along the top of the bar. It's best to tack the paper down for this. Then I set the tree on the drawdown stand and mark out the cut for the skirts.

On the special tree I use, I sometimes use a radical skirt design. We put the rigging in the skirt so all this can be figured out on the paper pattern. Low-down rigging offers extra stability—it tends to keep the saddle from moving around on the horse. We've tested this extensively and it works.

How radical, how deep to make the skirt, depends on the saddle buyer. Twelve-inches deep is what I consider regular. Dropping down two inches—a fourteen-inch-deep skirt—is a bit radical. Making the skirts sixteen-inches deep is very radical and the client should know that a very short cinch is needed for so deep a skirt.

Some time ago a friend gave me some old *Western Horseman* magazines from the forties. *Western Horseman* was then a California product and contained a number of articles by Luis B. Ortega. I had met Don Luis back in 1953 so I was interested in his writing. One of his articles told how it was possible to keep a center fire saddle on a horse. They used a rigging so low it came down to the center of the horse's barrels. And they used a short wide cinch that covered a lot of area.

At that time I had a filly in training with a terrible back. She was flat on top with slabby sides. She needed a very wide saddle but all we had rocked around on her. This caused her to be irritable and to wring her tail and act agitated.

One of my old saddles had rigging that was working loose due to rotting leather. I took the skirts off and made new skirts, sixteen-inches deep. They worked very well. The filly could be cinched looser and stopped wringing her tail. I made a cinch for this that is 26-inches long rather than the usual 30 inches. The cinch buckle is 3½-inches wide rather than 3 inches and I put 25 strands in the cinch rather than the usual 19.

To check out skirt design, it's a good idea to send for some catalogs from saddlemakers. See what you like and design your skirts accordingly.

You want to cut your skirt out so that you'll have 1½ inches in front of the bar and 3 inches or more behind the bar. This measurement will shorten a bit when you mold the skirt to the bar. You want to end up with about one inch of leather in front of the bar. How much you leave behind the bar depends on the buyer. On a really short-backed horse, you cut down the back accordingly, but I would say that the minimum is two inches of skirt behind the back of the bar.

When rigging in the skirts, take great care to put the rigging in the proper position. The rigging must be the same on both sides. If you're going to be off a little, be off up and down, not sideways. Being off sideways would make the saddle pull crookedly on the horse.

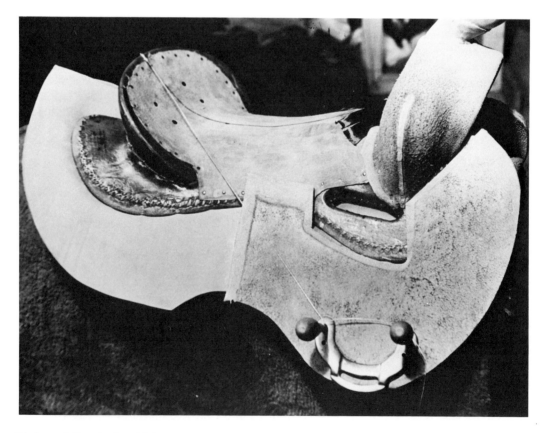

Lining up the rigging plates.

The best way I know to check this is to put a small nail on top of the cantle directly in the center. Take a string, tie a loose loop to the nail, and measure down to the rigging. Ink the measurement spot on the string. Measure the other side. The measurements should be very nearly the same.

Hold the rigging in place and draw around it with a felt-tipped pen. Make sure it's straight with the ground. You don't want a tipped rigging on the finished product. Eyeballing it is the best way, I think.

Leather parts can be cut out before work on the saddle begins. Most saddlemakers do this. It doesn't matter that much one way or the other though work goes more smoothly if you cut parts first. It'll save you leather—you can juggle patterns around to make the best use of the hide. You can get these patterns from an old saddle you like or save the patterns from your first saddle. You now have a skirt pattern. Make it a bit oversize so you can cut it down precisely.

We usually set the rigging at the ⅞ position. With the full double rig, you have to use a narrow cinch or you'll rub the horse's elbows. The full double rig is directly under the fork of the saddle. It bisects the swell. Set the ⅞ rig back from this about one inch.

Make suds with some good saddle soap and saddle soap the side of leather. After it's dried a bit, lay the pattern on the leather. Use a scratch awl to draw on the leather. Turn the pattern over for the other skirt. It's hell when you forget to do this and cut two left skirts. It usually means you'll need another side of leather to complete the saddle.

Cut the skirts out with the end of your round knife. Soak them for a few minutes and put them in a plastic sack to case overnight. You can be cutting out other parts, covering stirrups, or making a flank cinch while skirts are casing. Of course, you can be smart and cut them out and case them ahead of time.

There are various ways to ready leather. One saddlemaker says that you should soak the leather for hours and place parts between sheets of paper. If you use the plastic sack, you don't need to soak the leather very long for the humidity inside the plastic sack will soon have the leather thoroughly wet, and it will stay that way until you're ready to use it. However, don't leave leather in the sack more than a couple of days or it might mold. If you get any mold in a sack, throw the sack away and use a new one.

Put your carpet piece on the bench. Lay the cased skirt in place on the tree. Set a couple of small nails to hold it in place. The wet leather won't slip around much but it's terrible trying to keep dry leather in place on the tree.

Tap along the top line with a mallet. Then take your rub stick and rub the top line. Before you get too far along, set the tree on the stand and check out your rigging. Make sure it's in the correct spot. If all looks well, put the tree on the bench and tack the skirt in place so it won't shift. A dozen ¾-inch nails should do it. Don't set them in all the way for you'll soon be pulling them out.

Before going too far, check your skirts by laying one skirt over the other. You'll usually find that one skirt has shrunk more than the other. They won't match even though both have been cut exactly the same.

I'll tack the long (wet-leather) skirt in place by putting in about six ³/₄-inch slick box nails—not all the way in. Then I'll match the back of both skirts and tack the short one back in place. Setting my scratch awl to pull, I'll drive it through the leather into the tree and slowly stretch the short skirt to match the long skirt. The stretched skirt will then be secured the same as the long skirt so that it will dry the same length.

Take your rub stick and rub along the edge of the bars. Really press down for you're forming a seat for the leather. Take some slick short nails with heads and set

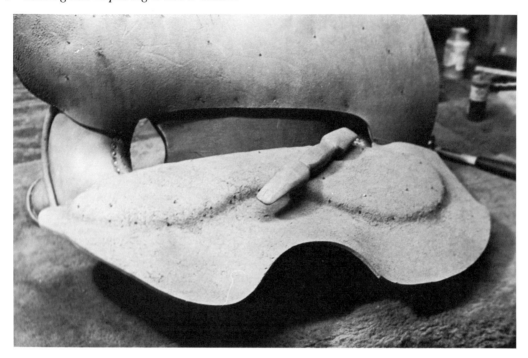

Above and right: *Mold skirts to tree and tack in place.*

them every few inches into the edge of the bars. When all this is dry, you'll have the deep impression of the bars formed into the skirts. It's then an easy matter to get the skirts back into the right place. You'll be putting them on and taking them off quite a few times before the saddle's finished.

When the skirt has formed by nailing it in place (no seated nails), sew the back of the skirts together in three or four places. Just punch a few awl holes opposite each other. This tack-type sewing just holds the back of the skirts even as they dry.

While waiting for the leather to dry in place, you can work on the sandwich piece that will be the top cover of the rigging. Make a paper pattern for it. This piece is used when you rig in the skirts. Other methods will be discussed later.

When the paper pattern looks pretty good, put it on your leather, scratch the design, and cut it out. Remember to reverse your pattern for the other side. Cut oversize.

Check your skirt measurement when it's dried out. You cut ½-inch oversize on your pattern. When you formed the skirts around the bars, you probably used up the ½ inch and the fit should be pretty fair.

I like to sew my back jockeys to the skirts so these can be fitted at this time. Make a paper pattern. Cut oversize edges but fit correctly against the cantle back. Tack the paper in place. Set the tacks where the back conchas will go.

Make sure you get a good fit on the back of the skirts where they come together. If you've cut oversize, you'll have an overlap at that place. When the skirts are dry, mark the places where the skirts should be cut down, take them off the tree, cut them down to correct size and put them back on the tree. Check it out. You may have to take them off again for more fitting. Don't get impatient. Skirts use a lot of leather and you don't want to waste them.

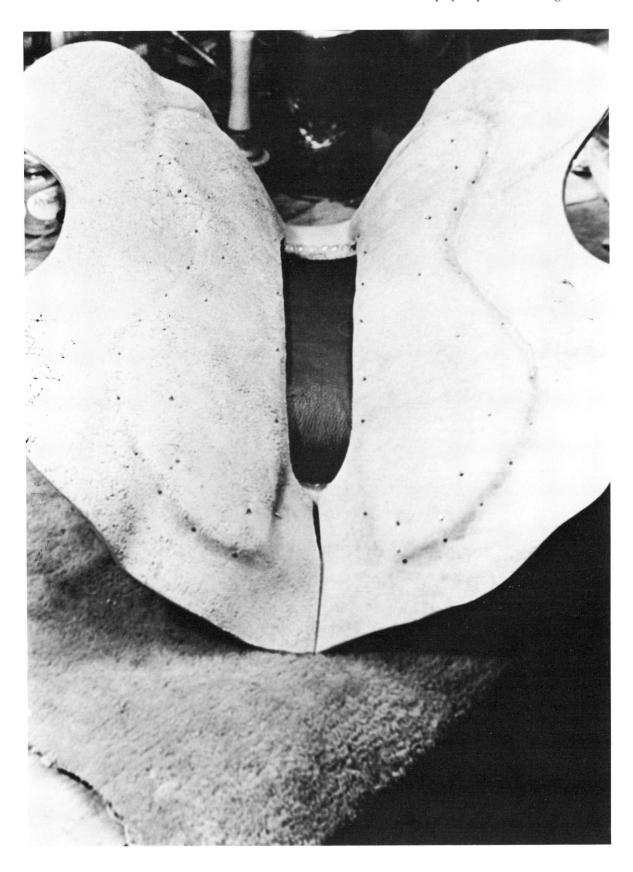

Paper pattern of rigging-plate sandwich.

Cut out two pieces that cover the rigging—the sandwich pieces—and tack in place. Leave them slightly oversized. Scratch the leather to be cemented and then cement these two pieces to the skirts.

OK, the front pieces are cemented on the skirts and the back jockeys are cut out. Don't cement the back jockeys on yet.

Take the skirts off the tree. You should know exactly where the rigging should go. Look at your rigging plates. They should be exactly the same size—but there's a good chance that the rivet holes won't line up the same on both plates. If they're different, use a marker pen to designate left from right.

Lay the rigging plate on the leather. Take a scratch awl and mark the center of the rivet holes. If you use #9 rivets, take an $^{11}/_{64}$ bit and carefully drill holes through the leather. Most punches are tapered so a punched hole wouldn't give you as good a fit for your rivet as the hole drilled with the electric drill and proper bit.

You can drop a couple of scratch awls through the rivet holes to make sure the plates don't slip while laying on the leather. You'll notice that the plates have indentations where they're supposed to have the leather fit. Carefully scratch out the place where you must cut to put in the plate. Make your cut.

Dampen the leather. Slip the rigging plates in place. They should line up all right. Rivet them in place. If you use a bench-top anvil for this, put a piece of paper on it or you'll get black marks on the leather. However, oxalic acid will remove the marks if you mess up a little.

Trim excess sheepskin from skirts.

At this point I like to wet the leather, press it down around the rigging plates, mark it, and sew them in. This is added insurance that the rigging won't loosen up. If it does loosen and wobble around, it'll wear out the rivets. I also sew a line under the bottom of the tree bars .

It's now time to glue on the sheepskin. Lay the skirts on the sheepskin. Draw around them with a marker pen. Apply contact cement to skirt and sheepskin. When dry, cement in place. Take a sharp knife and cut the excess sheepskin from the skirts. I think it's best to leave at least ¼ inch of sheepskin sticking out around the skirts. Of course, you've pressed the sheepskin down firmly all over the skirt, working from the center out. The sheepskin must form around the deep impression you made when you molded the skirts.

You now have a choice. You can sew the sheepskin to the skirts by hand or take all this to a shop where they have sewing machines. We do it by hand. One reason for this is that we only sew to the place where the back jockeys fit. Sewing in the back jockeys is usually done later.

The edge of the sheepskin must be trimmed and bevelled back. This is done for appearances—you don't see ragged sheepskin sticking out around the edges. It also makes hand stitching the edges easier. Any good shears will do. I use regular sheep shears.

Dampen the leather around the edge and put down a groove to sew in. Don't put the groove too close to the edge. You'll find it worth your while to make a large stitching pony like mine for the sewing chore. Mark stitch holes with a #5 or #6 stitch marker and sew the sheepskin in place.

Sewing the sheepskin to the skirts in the author's special clamp.

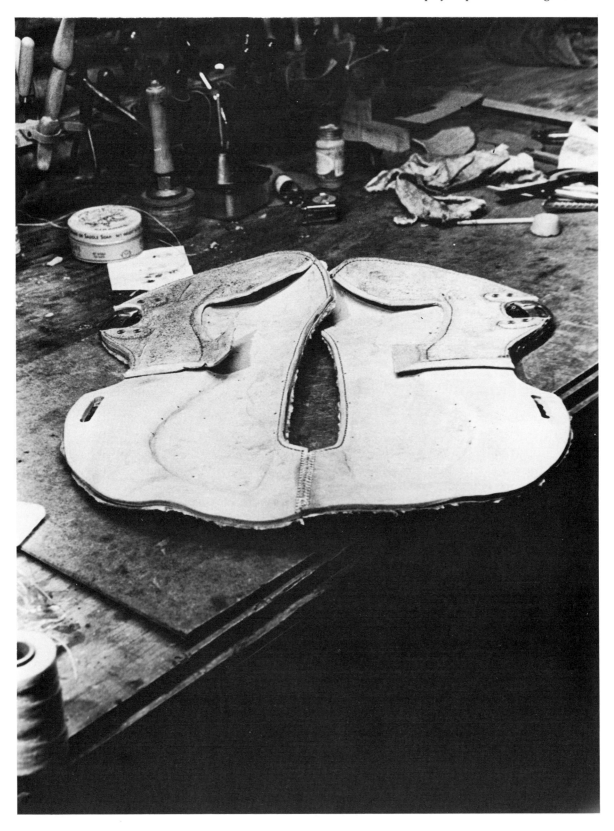

Sew skirt backs together.

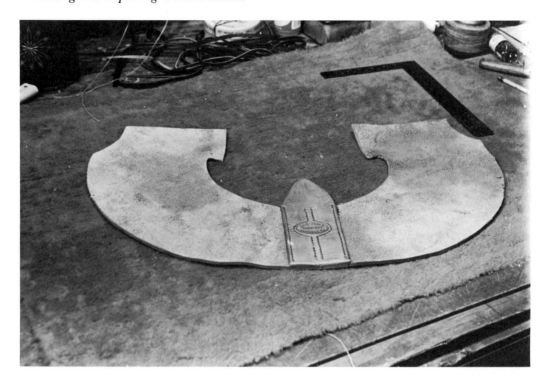

Sew shield to back of jockeys.

The next step is to sew or lace the skirts together at the back. Use the groover and stitch marker if you sew. I use two needles, nylon waxed lacing thread, and sew them together—though I use a lacing stitch. You can sew on a patch. You can punch holes and lace them together.

Put the skirts back on the tree and tack in place. This is easy since you've molded them to shape around the bars. Line up the old tack holes around the edge. Make sure the skirts are exactly in place.

Check the fit of the back jockeys. If something's wrong, now's the time to correct it. Your back rigging for the billets that carry the flank strap are set between the back billets and skirt so this needs to be checked out. You can buy metal back rigging plates or set in a piece of rawhide to stiffen and strengthen this back slot. We mostly use rawhide.

If all fits well, fasten the jockeys together by lacing or by sewing on a shield. I use a shield. Some saddlemakers lace through both jockeys and skirts. I put my saddler's stamp on the shield. To get the shield to fit just right, I check things out on the work bench and contact the shield to the jockeys. The shield is then sewn to the jockeys. Don't sew the back edge. You'll do this later, when you sew the jockeys to the skirts.

When the jockeys are ready, scratch the leather and contact cement them to the skirts. Don't cement over the slot for the back rigging. If you do get some cement at that point, you can work it loose later.

You should have a couple of pieces of rawhide soaking. When you're sewing and get within four or five inches from the back slot, stop and fit the rawhide in place. Sew in the rawhide. When you've finished sewing around the jockeys, sew around the rawhide-enforced slots. Then cut out the rawhide that covers the slots. Skirts are finished except for the edging and edge polishing.

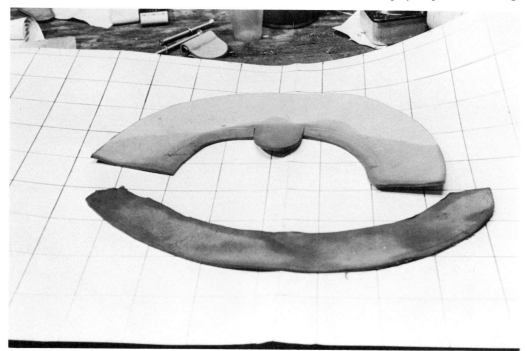

Cantle back and cantle filler.

Cantle Back

The skirts are fitted to the bare cantle back. When you finally pop the skirts on after the cantle back is put on, the fit will be very snug—the way you want it.

We're doing this saddle without a Cheyenne roll. We'll use a cantle filler. This is a piece of leather, two to three inches wide and long enough to go clear around the cantle, shaped to fit the contour of the cantle. Don't use stiff leather for this. Skive one edge very thin. Tack the filler on the cantle, skived edge down. Tack about ¾ inch down from the top of the cantle. Start in the center and work out both ways. You'll have to do a little pulling and stretching but it shouldn't take very long.

The cantle back is cut to fit the back of the cantle. You'll have a fold rim that lays on the tree bars and a tab that goes up under the cantle. Skive the leather where it folds over the bars. Tack it on wet and let it dry out. Don't tack anywhere but on the folded leather over the bars.

When the cantle back has dried out, scratch it and the cantle filler. Scratch the rawhide below the filler. Contact cement the cantle back in place. This is all you do with it until you're ready to sew on the cantle binding.

Regular Skirts, Rigging, and Jockeys

There certainly isn't room in this book to put in descriptions of every way to do things in saddlemaking, but I will briefly describe regular rigging, skirts, and jockeys.

Cantle back and filler in place.

Side view of cantle back and filler in place.

Rigging straps used to run clear over the fork, but since trees are much stronger today, this isn't needed. The full double and ⁷/₈ rigging fit under the swell. I prefer to double this rigging and have screws go through both leather pieces. Rigging leathers are sometimes laced together with only one piece of leather screwed into the three. This makes a somewhat flatter job but I don't feel it's quite as strong as the other way.

The back rigging can be put in with a variety of methods. Some saddlemakers run a strap completely over the back of the bars. Other riggings are attached to the bars. I feel that publicizing super strength for the back rigging is a gimmick— super strength isn't needed there. If this sells saddles, more power to the gimmick. However, most back riggings come apart when the billets tear at the flank cinch buckles.

The front and back riggings are usually hobbled together. An inch strap suffices. It's riveted or laced. This hobble is subject to wear from friction since the fenders and stirrup straps rub it. When repairing an old saddle with hobble straps, you'll usually find them about worn through or long gone.

I'll use drawings of many popular plate riggings. They're self-explanatory. These flat plate riggings are pretty good for lowering the rigging or putting it just where you want it. With a ¾, ⅝ or center fire- plate rigging, you can get the stirrup strap in front of the rigging and eliminate the lump under the knee from the latigo.

When the rigging isn't in the skirt, the skirt just cushions the horse. Old timers tacked them in place with saddle strings run clear through the tree to help hold things together. For this, two holes are bored with a ¹/₄-inch or larger drill at all points where the conchas go. The sheepskin is cut between the holes so the strings won't make a bulge that could rub the horse. They're pounded flat.

When such a skirt is used, the back jockeys are cosmetic—just used to cover the back of the bars. They add no strength to the finished product. Conchas and tacks hold them in place. The saddle strings run through back jockeys, tree, skirts and conchas.

When the back jockeys are sewn to the skirts, they do add strength to the whole rigging, for they're attached to the tree in five places plus the stitching.

Differences Between Illustrated Saddles and Others

Any style saddle can be made as illustrated—with the rigging in the skirts. As a rider, I think the in-skirt rigging offers a wrap around effect that holds the saddle on the horse better than the conventional D-rings rigging. I've used both.

The conventional saddle's skirts aren't secured well enough to have the rigging in them. They're on there to distribute the weight of saddle and rider, and to attach the sheepskin to. The sheepskin pads the horse's back and holds the saddle blanket in place. There are no skirts on such saddles as the English and McClellan.

To make the conventional saddle's skirts stiffer, a liner's usually used. This liner is skived thin at the bottom part of the bars—it fits around the front, bottom and back of the saddle.

To hold the conventional skirt firmly up to the bars, a couple of holes are punched through the skirts at various places. Pieces of latigo run through these holes and are tacked to the top of the bars. This method is used when the back jockeys are separate pieces—not attached to the skirts. In time, these latigo pieces

Rigging Styles or Methods & Positions

Leather folded *over* ring, hand sewn and riveted.

Leather folded *under* ring, buck stitched.

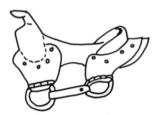

Leather folded *under* dee, thong laced.

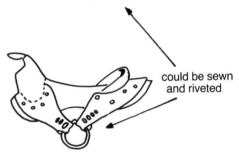

could be sewn and riveted

Leather folded *under*, thong laced.

Leather folded *under* dee, riveted.

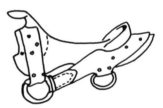

Leather folded *under* ring and dee and riveted. Connecting strap from back rigging folded *over* ring, hand sewn and thonged.

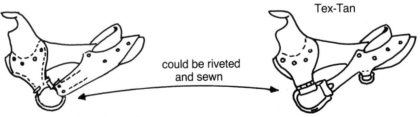

Tex-Tan

could be riveted and sewn

Leather folded *under* ring, thonged *over* outside of doubled leather and buckstitched up toward tree.

Front leathers folded *under* and thonged back, dee riveted.

Various riggings. (Courtesy William Smith)

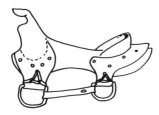

Leather folded *under*, thonged.

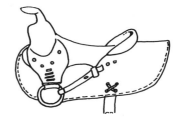

Ring rig thonged. Connecting strap riveted to metal dee riveted to skirt.

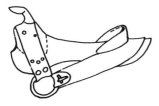

3/4 ring standard riveted and thonged.

Flatplate Styles

Ray Hole's Style

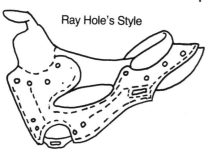

Leather doubled and stitched, plate riveted between the two leathers.

Gentry Rigging Style, Utahn Saddle Co.

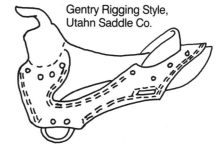

Leather doubled and double stitched on edges. Dee ring sandwiched between leathers and riveted.

Tex-Tan Style

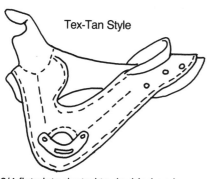

3/4 flat plate riveted to doubled and stitched leather.

Porter's Flat Plate Style

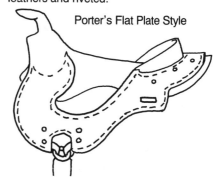

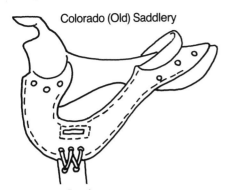

Colorado (Old) Saddlery

All leather flat rig.

Rigging in Skirt Styles

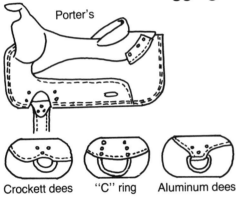

Porter's

Crockett dees   "C" ring   Aluminum dees

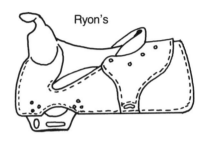

Ryon's

Handmade stainless steel plate with breast collar slots.

break and let the skirts sag away from the bars—one reason I don't care for the system.

There are so many ways to rig saddles, I'd best just show a few popular ones. My friend Bill Smith of Lincoln, California is to be credited with the sketches.

Fenders–Stirrups, Straps

I want to place the fenders on the saddle sometime before I fit the seat. This helps in seat design if you're working with a forward-seat saddle. The design we use features a dropped-down back fender. This gives you more fender while still having a full foot of strap on the fender for adjustment. If you don't use the dropped-down design, you have to use a shorter fender. Then the bottom of the fender can catch on the top of the rider's boot.

The way a saddle rides is influenced a great deal by fender design. You can use an extreme forward-cut fender to put the rider's legs forward. However, if you put such a fender on a saddle with a built-up front, there's no way a rider can raise himself up in the saddle. He's locked back against the cantle and can't get up over the center of gravity. The regular fender will keep the center of gravity farther back and he'll be a bit more flexible.

The forward-cut fender is ideal for level-ride or low-front saddles. These rigs are getting more popular every day. They overcome the objections that in the western saddle you can't get your legs forward, and that the slope back forces you to ride the cantle of the saddle.

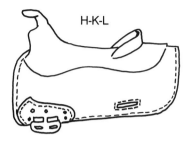

H-K-L

Full double, 7/8 double or 3/4 double rig positions.

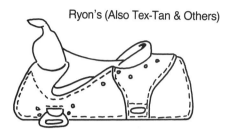

Ryon's (Also Tex-Tan & Others)

Stainless steel plates

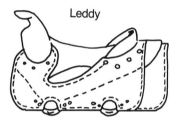

Leddy

Full double in skirt.

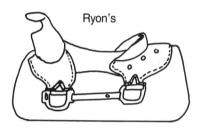

Ryon's

Full double with handmade stainless steel breast harness, slotted dees.

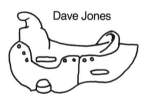

Dave Jones

Forward slots rig in skirts.

Rodeo Shop, Ft. Worth

Stainless steel dees covered with double bull hide.

In my old *Western Horseman* copies I found an article lauding the forward-cut fender. The author used charts and diagrams to show how the forward-cut fender would revolutionize western riding. I think he was right. The difference is astonishing. The old bronc saddle fenders attached to stirrup straps—the straight fender—made for a ride about as bad as a ride could be.

Using forward slots, the forward fender isn't needed. We try to make a graceful cut but our fenders aren't actually forward—or aren't radically forward.

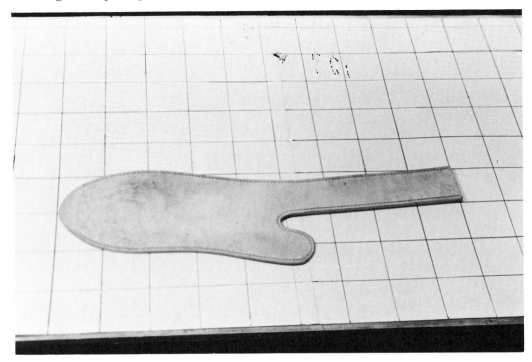

A fender.

With the forward slots, a fender must be a little shorter than a conventional one. This is because the slots are lower down than the regular position. Thus, the seat jockey will be deeper and you just want the seat jockey to cover the top of the fender. I make the fender for forward-slot saddles on the average 14-inches long from the top to the bottom (the top of the curved cut at the bottom). Then the strap on the fender is 12 inches from this measurement. The straps that are riveted average 30-inches long and are cut $2^7/8$-inches wide. If you cut a 3-inch strap a full 3-inches wide, it may not allow the Blevins stirrup buckle hood to work easily. This is especially true with heavy-duty leather. Naturally, you'd make a longer fender and strap for a long-legged person and a shorter fender and strap for a short-legged person.

The seat fits just above the bottom edge of the skirts. You can figure out the fender length of a regular stock saddle by keeping this in mind.

A wear leather is set inside the bottom stirrup strap. Ours are about 14-inches long for we sew this strap to the bottom stirrup strap. The most common way to attach this strap is to rivet the Blevins buckles in, bend the stirrup strap the way it'd bend in use, and rivet it to the fender. The wear strap should be shorter than the stirrup strap to make up for the bend in the leathers. However, it isn't necessary to do this when the straps are stitched together. They're easily put into the correct position when they're soaked and shaped.

The Blevins buckles can be set with the knobs in or out. The usual and handiest way is to set the knobs out. This sets the excess stirrup strap out. You can make the rig more adjustable but less handy by reversing the buckle and running the stirrup strap inside. This puts the end of the stirrup strap under the stirrup roller.

Putting in Blevins buckles.

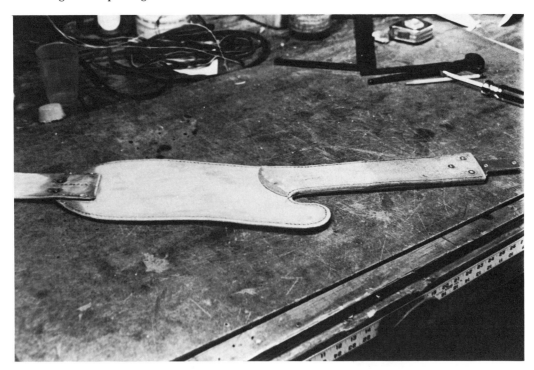

Stirrups strap and Blevins buckle in. Stirrups strap riveted and sewn in.

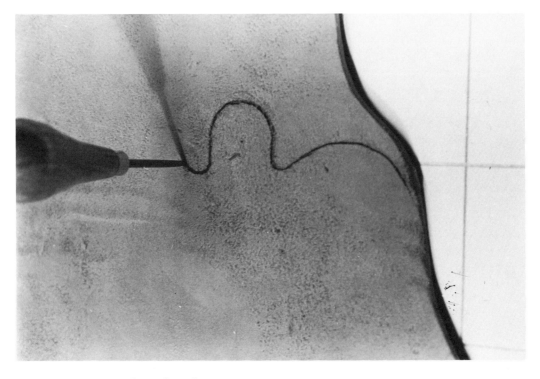

Spots to be cut out at base of cantle.

Our procedure goes like this: Cut the fenders from a pattern to the correct size. Glue them with contact cement to the stirrup straps on the fenders. Then groove them, mark, edge and sew. If the whole fender isn't to have stitching all around it, stitching will stop at the bottom of the fender. Since the wear leathers have been cut a bit wide, cut them down to size after cementing—the cut will then be exact and neat. Last, rivet and sew stirrup straps to the fenders.

To shape them for the owner, soak them until they're pliable and put them on the saddle. Twist them to proper shape. Run a 2''x2'' through the stirrups (the saddle is on the drawdown stand). The drawdown bar goes over the 2''x2'' that runs through the stirrups. Pull down tight. Let the straps and fenders dry out on the stand. This will help the breaking-in process a great deal.

Fitting the Seat

One of the toughest jobs in saddlemaking is fitting the seat, not only because you're working with leather that must be stretched a lot and can't be made well from a close-cut pattern, but because you're also going to waste a lot of money if you do a poor job. A seat takes a mighty chunk out of a side of leather. Go at it slowly and cautiously.

Put the skirts on the saddle—or, at least, one skirt. At this point, you'll have them sewn together if you use my method. You need to follow the skirt contour with the seat. Your leather should be well cased. The heavy leather always goes to the front. Cut a V in the front center so you can always find center immediately.

Lay the rough-cut seat on the tree. Press the back down—mold it down to the cantle with your hands. You might want to use a leather smasher here if you have one. You should get it down enough to be able to mark two points. Run your sewing awl through the leather at the base of the cantle on both sides but only after you're sure you have the leather well down and centered. It's best to put your drawdown strap over the seat and draw it down. This will help you see if it's centered or not. If you wrinkle the leather a little at this point, rub the wrinkles out later. Pulling it down with the strap will make it hoove up in front and back. Right now, you're mainly concerned about the leather at the base of the cantle. Find the spots—the base of the cantle—and mark these spots with your awl. Punch clear through the leather.

Take the seat off the tree and put it on the bench. Take your scratch awl and mark out a slight arc from the awl points outward. This arc is about ¾-inch long. The arc is where the seat leathers pass over the cantle binding. Now cut out the seat buttons. You can cut these with a one-inch half-round punch or mark out the button to suit yourself. Now make a mark from the end of the seat button running back and down out to the edge of the leather. Mark the other side the same and carefully cut on your lines.

Put the seat back on the tree. The back will now lay down flat. Center everything carefully and put the drawdown strap in place. Cinch'er down.

Start marking and cutting out from the center of the handhold. Keep a margin of leather in front of the groundseat at the handhold. Next, you want to decide how high you want your seat leather to ride up on the fork. It should ride up higher on a swell fork saddle than on a fork roper. Keeping it up there covers up the nails you've set when you anchored down the fork cover and eliminates unsightly gaps between fork and seat.

When you start cutting out the leather around the swell of the fork, use a French edger or a shoemaker's lip knife so the knife point won't dig into the

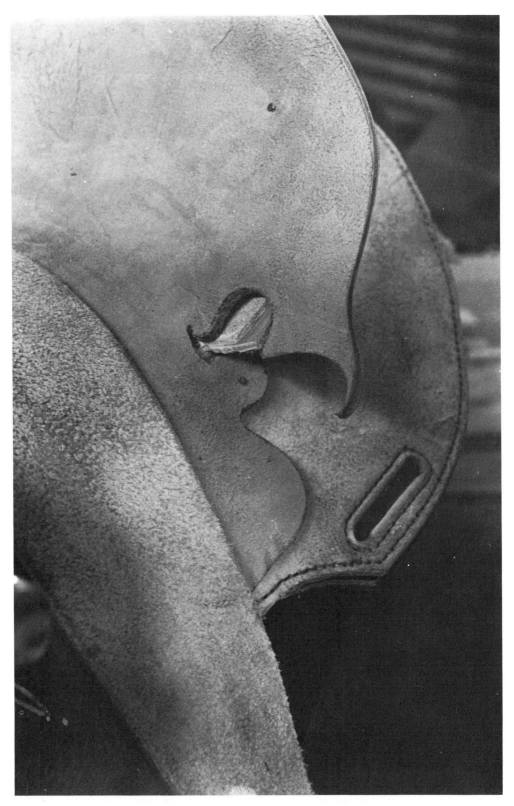

It's easy to get the back of the seat down after the buttons have been cut out.

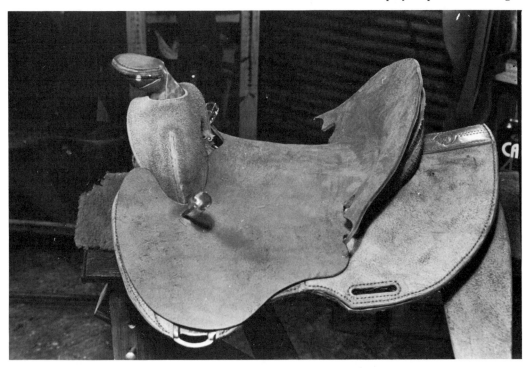

Tack the seat buttons down and stretch the seat with an awl.

leather on the fork cover. Cut a little, press down, check, and cut a little more. Make timid cuts at first. Leave the leather way up on the fork—you can always cut more away later. The leather under the swell can fool you. Cut it where you *think* it ought to be cut and you'll have a huge gap there when you're finished. A very shallow cut will often end up being just right.

When this cut has been made on the left side—when it looks just right to you—take the seat off the tree, fold it in the center, mark the uncut side from the cut side and cut it identically.

Some saddlemakers stretch the leather forward quite taut before making the cut around the fork. To do this, tack the seat buttons down to hold the back of the seat in place. Take a large scratch awl and punch a hole directly under the swell. Set the awl to stretch forward. Pull the leather forward with the awl. Then drive the awl securely into the tree and let it hold the seat while you cut around the fork. When the seat is finished, a screw and counter sink washer will be set in the hole.

The screw under the fork can somewhat restrict the forward swing of the stirrups. The seat can be put on without stretching at that point. You may have to stretch from the spot in front of the fork where the front conchas and latigo holders go.

The fit of the front of the seat and the seat jockeys depends somewhat upon the artistic ability of the saddlemaker. For our specialized saddle with forward stirrups, I follow the line of the skirts. If I'm doing a radical skirt, then I also have a radical fit to the seat. The lowest part of the seat jockeys is forward since it's a forward saddle. I'd suggest sending for a few catalogs from good saddlemakers to get an idea of different designs. Use what appeals to you. Some of my friends really collect stuff like old catalogs, saddle pictures in magazines, etc. If you have a lot of interest, you'll do the same. These fellows are always trying to better themselves and will continue to do so when they're eighty. They're always interested in the work of others and really latch onto any new ideas they see or hear of.

How much seat leather to leave above the cantle depends upon the type cantle binding you use. I leave a couple of inches when I'm just using a cantle binding. You want quite a bit more than this when putting on a Cheyenne roll.

The line to follow for the seat front in front of the fork is usually ¼ inch back from the edge of the skirt. You can cut the front off flush with the skirts and then use a scratch compass to mark your line ¼ inch. All lines should flow and be pleasing to the eye.

When the seat is cut out on the left side, take it off the tree, fold it in the center, and mark the lines you'll cut on to cut the other side. Put it back on the tree for a check after the seat's been completely cut out. If all's well, take it off the tree, edge it and then polish the edges.

An old saddlemaker once wrote to me about some unorthodox saddle work I had published in an article. He said, "That's the way. If it works, use it."

So I'm going to tell you about a bastard method I sometimes use to fit up a seat. It works, is quick and I've never messed up a seat when using this method.

Making a seat pattern is difficult because the paper won't conform— it can't be shaped and stretched like wet leather. I have a leather pattern that came from a seat I'd ruined. I cut this old seat in half to make the pattern.

To use this old leather pattern, I ink a line directly down the center of the ground seat. My leather pattern has been soaked until it's thoroughly wet and pliable. It's placed on the tree and fitted up as best I can. It shows me where I have to change a pattern to get a correct fit.

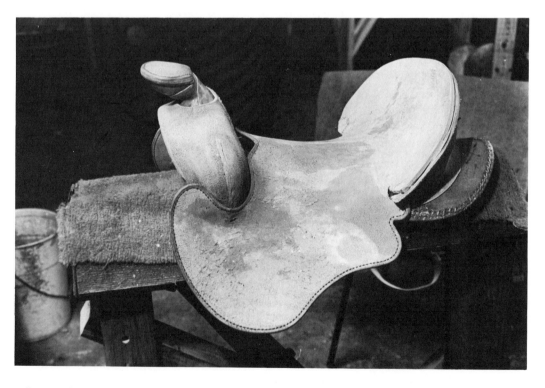

This seat has been stitched.

I then fold a piece of pattern paper directly in the center and lay the leather pattern on it, allowing for the changes I need to make. I'll only rough cut the seat from my pattern but it allows me to precisely cut the front around the fork and to get the exact points at the base of the cantle. When these cuts are made, the new seat can easily be shaped. The exact cut can be drawn with the wet new seat in place on the tree.

Stitching around the seat and fenders looks very nice—it helps keep the leather from stretching and checking. This is up to you. We do such stitching by hand. If it looks like too much stitching for you, the seat and fenders can be taken to a saddle or shoe shop. The edges can be dyed before polishing if you wish.

When you finally are ready to put the seat down, you may have to dampen it or case it to get it to come into place. Set it on the tree. Tack the seat buttons down. Pull the front forward with your awls. Put the drawdown leather in place. Put the spreader bar in place. Carefully snug the drawdown strap. Check for wrinkles. If you find any, loosen up the strap and rub the wrinkles out with a stick. When all's centered, cinch 'er down. Make sure the seat leather is pulled up on the fork where you want it to be. Tack the front down where your latigo holders will go. Let the seat dry out and shape.

There are a couple of ways to glue down the seat. You can contact cement the seat to the ground-seat. This is quick. The disadvantage is that you can't work the seat around. When you put it down, put it down right the first time. Don't press it down. Lay it lightly in place and check. If it is a little off, you can jerk it loose and try again. Actually, since it's shaped and stretched, it falls in place pretty easily. A good place to start from is the seat buttons. If you have them even, chances are good that it'll all line up.

Of course, you can use a slow-drying glue such as Dexterine to hold the seat down. With this glue, you have all the time in the world to move the seat around to get it just so. There's one problem. Most cantles are slightly dished. The leather over the dish in the cantle won't shape down to it with this slow glue unless you weight it with a sand bag, as described on page 52.

Cheyenne Roll

You may want a Cheyenne roll on your saddle. If so, the cantle filler must stick up as high as you want the roll to be. Two inches is a common width for a Cheyenne roll. The cantle back must be at least this high. I like to have 2½ inches of leather sticking up for the filler and the cantle back. Don't glue them together before you bend them down! Both should be damp when you bend them. Bend the cantle back down first. The leather must "break" sharply at a 90° angle or more where the roll starts. Rub hard with your rub stick under the cantle to keep the leather up tight where it bends. You want it right up snug to the cantle for you have to stitch right through there. Rub the top of the roll with a stick or a leather smasher.

Next, bend the cantle filler back over the cantle back. It will plop down into place easily. Rub with the smasher to get a sharp break line. Let both dry out. After they're dry, lift the cantle filler enough to apply contact cement. Cement cantle back and cantle filler together.

When you drop your seat in place and push the back edge down, you'll notice that you have spaces where the cantle binding or Cheyenne roll will go. These should be filled. They're where the side buttons came from. There would be a hollow place if these weren't filled.

Find some scrap leather the same thickness and texture as the back of the seat. Cut to fit these places. You can contact cement these pieces in.

To check out your fit precisely, pop stitch the back of the seat to the cantle filler and back. At the break of the cantle on each side, taper the roll down until you have a half inch or so at the point where the seat passes over the binding.

Measure and cut evenly the width you want your Cheyenne roll. Edge with your spokeshave or large edge beveler.

Your roll cover should be a bit oversized. Case it. You want give to the leather, so cut it from the belly. The most flanky edge will go underneath the roll. Groove, mark, and edge the exposed side. Tack an end under the seat and pull it across the roll. When you have it stretched smoothly, set a few small nails through the stitch marks to hold it in place. Tack down the other edge. Work the leather up under the roll. Use a stick after you've pushed and kneaded it as much as possible with your hands. You may have a few bulges under the roll that just won't work out. The more extreme the roll, the more likely you'll have these bulges. Carefully cut them out with a leather knife.

You can apply Dexterine to the seat and Cheyenne roll before stitching. If you do so, you'll need your sandbag on the cantle as it dries. Or you can contact cement the whole thing. The roll cover should be pretty dry if you do this.

Sew the cover on. Pull out the small nails as you go. Never use blue tacks for this for they turn the leather black. Of course, if you've used contact cement, the leather will be dry when you sew so the little nails can be pulled out ahead of time. Stitch neatly. It's slow, tough going for you don't have much needle room. You may have to use pliers to pull the needle from the underside. Don't rush it. When saddles with the extremely low roping cantles were in style, putting the Cheyenne roll on them was a real pain.

Regular Cantle Binding

The regular cantle binding is easier to put on than the Cheyenne roll except for one thing. Both sides of the stitching show.

You start the same. The seat, cantle filler, and cantle back are cemented together. There should be at least an inch sticking up when you cement them. Take the glass pliers and crimp around the cantle. This gives a definite line to follow. Use the scratch compass and mark a line up about $1/2$ inch above the crimped line. Carefully cut on this line. Smooth and edge. I use the spokeshave for this.

The cantle binding is a full two-inches wide and is cut from belly leather because it has to stretch. Mark, groove, and edge the front side. There are a few ways to prepare the back. You have a lot of leather to sew through and you want the back of the cantle to look neat—neat stitches or none showing at all.

Stitches Show   Put some Dexterine on the cantle binding, nail it down under the seat, stretch it tightly over the cantle, and secure it under the seat on the other side. Now line up the groove and marks with the crimped line. Set a few brads or small nails through some of the stitch marks to hold everything in place. You'll pull these nails out as you stitch.

Rub the back of the binding with your rub stick. The original crimped line will show enough for you to know exactly where it is. Mark this line with your scratch awl. You can also mark it with your stitch marker. Run the awl through the whole binding, hit the line and try to hit those marks as much as possible. If the awl isn't coming out right, withdraw it and reinsert it.

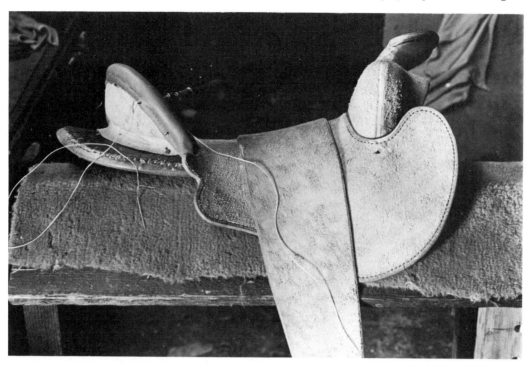

Sewing cantle binding.

The Slant Cut to Sew Into Hold your leather knife at an angle to make a half-inch cut through the leather on the stitch line back of the cantle. When you're ready to sew, push the top edge up, sew in this slit, and push the leather down over your stitches when you're finished. This makes a nice-looking cantle back.

Sewing in a Full Split Alan Dewey showed me this one. Part's hard and part's easy. You actually split the leather up about ¾ inch from the bottom of the outside of the cantle binding. The outside of the leather is pushed up for the stitching. You hold the leather on the edge of the workbench and carefully split it with the round knife. Take your time for the split must be exact. You can feel the blade with your finger. Check often to make sure you're cutting deep enough but not too deep. Practice on scrap leather. It sounds harder than it is. Your round knife must be razor sharp. When finished, let it dry, glue 'er down, and edge.

When sewing the cantle binding, it's a good policy to sew up about ¹⁄₁₆ inch above your crimp line to make sure your awl doesn't hit the tree. You can mark a second line for this—your stitch line—and set the nails that hold the binding in place through the higher line. Sew on the high line.

Attaching the Skirts

Put the tree on the carpeted bench. Work the back on first. When the back is loosely in place, set the rig on the drawdown stand. Use your rub stick as a lever to get the front pocket leathers over the front of the bars.

You'll notice that the back jockeys fit up against the cantle back pretty well. To get an even tighter fit, use your scratch awl on the tab at the cantle side of the

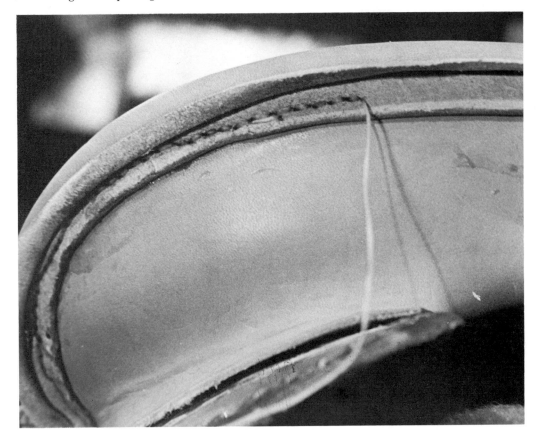

Sewing in a full split.

shield. Set the awl to bite and pull (saddle upside-down on the bench). When you've drawn the leather up snug, place two or three wallboard nails at the bottom of the cantle. You'll have the back pretty secure.

I like to use one-inch wallboard nails (ring shank) along the top line of the skirts. I think they're better there than screws. I also like wallboard nails to secure the edges of the leather to the top of the bars—the outer edges of the skirts that are under the seat. This leather has to be skived a bit so it won't form lumps. Screws tear up a lot more leather than the ring shanks.

Many saddlemakers and saddle-repair people object to ring-shank (wallboard) nails in that they're almost impossible to pull out for saddle repair. The hot dipped galvanized nail is preferred and should suit those who object to ring-shanked nails. The new galvanized nail is electroplated and is very slick—doesn't give the holding power of the old hot dipped nail.

The hot dipped galvanized nail is nearly a thing of the past. I recently found four 30-pound boxes of one-inch hot dipped galvanized nails—a lifetime supply. Better hunt up your supply of such nails while they're still available. If you have to buy longer hot dipped nails, you can always cut them down. The 1¼-inch hot dipped nail will probably be available for some time.

I use oval-head screws from Standard Saddle Tree Company to screw the skirts to the tree. Evenly spaced, I use about ten screws per side. First, I cut away a little wool at the screw site with a French edger. Then I make a hole with a large

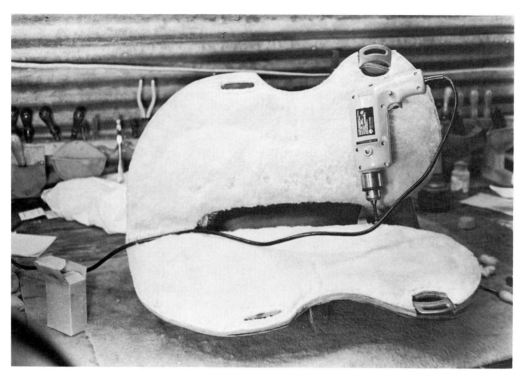

Use screws to secure the skirt to the tree.

awl. This hole is just deep enough to get the screw started. Then I use my variable speed reversible ½-inch drill to put the screws in. This drill has a setting on the trigger that allows me to set the screws just deep enough. I want to put the head slightly under the surface of the sheepskin. I need to add that I use pure Neatsfoot oil on the leather side of the skirts before I secure them to the tree. This leather never has another chance to be oiled so I consider oiling at the onset a must.

Stringing the Saddle

If you use leather conchas, you'll usually use eleven of them. On the left front concha spot, put on a latigo holder and a small concha. At the other spots (base of cantle, back of cantle), use two conchas.

Some years ago, I used to run the saddle strings through the bars. You have to drill a couple of holes at each concha site to do this. Between the holes on the underside, the sheepskin is cut out and the saddle string is pounded flat so it won't rub the horse. This method is still widely used but many saddlemakers feel that it weakens the tree. When you do use this method, use slotted conchas.

The method I like best is to use unslotted conchas and screw them to the tree. I use a drive awl, start the hole and use a power driver to seat the screws.

Rather than attaching the saddle strings to the saddle, I set small D-rings between the conchas. A piece of galvanized metal, cut, doubled and punched for the screw, is easy to make. The strings are hitched to this D-ring. The rider can leave them on, take them off, or use part of them as the occasion demands.

The rope strap can be put on by the doubled galvanized metal piece. I use lace leather for this unless the buyer specifies a heavy strap and buckle. Most knowledgeable riders want a rope strap that will break if they get caught in the rope. A slit is cut where the curve of the swell starts to break toward the horn. Glue is punched loose with a screwdriver and the metal with the D-ring on it is tapped into place. A hole is then punched through leather and metal so a brass pin or screw can secure the rope strap metal piece.

Latigos, Billets, and Back Cinch

As a rider, I dislike wide 2-inch latigos. I favor 1½-inch latigos and cut mine out that way. Six-foot latigos are long enough. For looks, I edge and paraffin the edges. Rub paraffin into a piece of light canvas, secure one end of the latigo and vigorously pull the canvas along the latigo *one way*. Don't rub back and forth.

Let me throw in a word for paraffin. When you're sewing something really tough and are having a hard time getting the awl to pierce the leather, rub the awl on a stick of paraffin between each thrust. It'll save you a lot of work.

You can rig the latigos the same on both sides. If so, you'll need two latigo holders. I like my latigo holders mounted outside the seat leather. Some folks want them under the front part of the seat ahead of the fork. If the latigos are the same on both sides, they can be easily adjusted from both sides when the saddle is cinched down on a horse. This is a good method for the person who rides a lot of different horses.

Many saddles are equipped with a doubled skirting leather billet for the off-side of the cinch. As a rider, I hate these. They're too heavy and stiff.

I do like the half-breed latigo for the off-side. It's widely used. The middle of the latigo goes around the cinch ring. Then the doubled latigo goes over the rigging ring or plate and back down to the cinch. The tongue of the cinch buckle secures the off half-breed latigo.

Some saddles still employ the tie-on method for the cinch. There are no tongues in the cinch itself so the latigos are brought up and secured with the cinch knot.

Secure the latigos to the rigging with a piece of lace leather. Punch an oval hole and two round holes. Figure to punch the oval where a person's nose would be. Then punch the two round holes where the eyes would be. Latigo is doubled and put through the oval hole. It separates and one piece of lace runs through the smaller holes. Then the ends run through the place where the lace starts—the oval hole. Pull this all up tight and the latigo is secured.

Back Billets

Your back billets are cut the size of the back-cinch buckle. I use 2-inch brass-plated flank cinch buckles (Walsalls) so we use 2-inch billets. Thirty inches long is about right. For fancy saddles, line with light latigo and stitch. They can be laced on or a keeper can be riveted on that the billet bends back into.

Normally the flank cinch is about 3-inches wide. Some customers order a very wide one—say 6-inches wide. This uses up a lot of leather so you should charge extra for it. I've found the extra-wide cinch to be of no practical value.

The billet keepers on the flank cinch are usually sewn on along the outer edge. You need space for this. If you use a 2-inch buckle, you need a half inch on

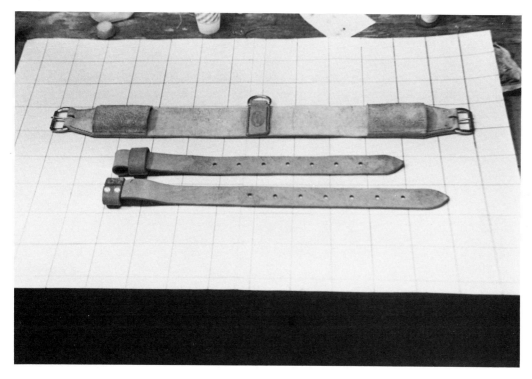

Billets and flank strap.

each side to play with, so you'd made a 3-inch-wide flank cinch. I use small nails to tack the keeper into place. They're removed as you sew.

From the horseman's viewpoint, the billet holder shouldn't be made to fit too snugly. When the rider has to force the billet down into the holder every time he saddles a horse, he'll soon cuss the saddlemaker. Just a simple little thing like this can cost a guy a lot of business. When I let the holders dry out, I leave two thicknesses of leather in them so they'll dry out oversized.

Covering Stirrups

I prefer to hand stitch the covering on the stirrups rather than lace them. The advantage of sewing over lacing is that you can get them on tighter. Lacing can get cut pretty easily and the leather will then start to work loose.

When we sell a saddle, we have a basic price. That saddle will have latigos and a cinch. There will be a tread and a chafe on the stirrup roller to protect the stirrup straps. If the stirrups are completely covered, we charge for it since there's a large amount of leather (and time) used when covering stirrups.

To fully cover stirrups, we use fairly heavy stiff leather on the outside while flanky stretchy leather is used on the inside. Take the bolts out of the stirrups. Cut the leather extra wide. Give yourself an inch clearance with the leather all the way around the stirrups. The novice has a tendency to cheat on leather—not to give himself enough to work with. Often this means doing it over at double the cost in leather.

Crimp stirrups covers with glass pliers to get a sewing line.

Contact cement the stirrups and the leather. If you dampen anything, dampen the flanky inside leathers, and dampen with a sponge rather than soak. Don't wet the side you want to glue.

Put the cemented leather in place and mold it to shape with your hands. Then use your rub stick to press and form the inside leather to the outside. When all is in shape, crimp along the edges with your glass pliers.

Scratch a line where you want to sew. Then groove with a freehand groover or a broad point in a swivel knife. Mark and stitch. Trim, edge, and polish the edges.

The holes in the stirrups are one inch down from the top. Cut out the leather over the holes. I use a drill for this. The chafe on the roller can be glued, sewn, and/or riveted to secure. Assemble the stirrup. Make sure you put the bolts in the same way they were installed when you bought them. The nut side goes toward the horse—slick round bolt part out. If there's excess bolt sticking out, cut it with a hack saw and tap the end with a hammer to rivet the nut on the bolt.

The bolt ends can be hidden. You just assemble the stirrup before glueing and stitching.

Covering the tread of the stirrup is the hardest part if you get a good tight fit. I don't like a loose tread. This needs to be a fairly heavy leather for it'll get a lot of wear. You can't mold it by hand very well. I either use a pattern I have or make one if it's an odd-size stirrup. The pattern is extra long. My stitching horse will hold a stirrup, so I set it in place, pull the leather up together as tight as possible, and tack or pop stitch to hold it in place. It still isn't tight.

Now I cut the leather down enough so that I can get my pliers on it. I'll pull and clamp my way along until I get a fair mark. Then I scratch a line that's wider at the ends than the center. This is because there's heavy wood in the center of the stirrup so the leather must stretch down a lot more at each end. I groove with my swivel knife and mark on both sides with the stitch marker. Then I sew, using heavy nylon thread. I lock stitch each stitch and take my time, allowing the leather to stretch as I sew. I know of no way to put on a tighter tread.

3

Saddle Variations and Repair

Variations

There are many variations in saddle making. When you make a conventional saddle, you can buy a metal ground seat (strainer) from Standard Saddle Tree Company or make one yourself from heavy-gauge galvanized metal. This is a one-piece strainer. You need to remember to cut plugs where the stirrup straps go and tack them in place before you fit the seat.

People will want patch seats, padded seats, etc. A patch seat is made from a piece of chap leather, usually rough side out, sewn to the seat. This is simply measuring and stitching. It must go on up under the cantle binding. A padded seat has padding such as foam rubber to make a softer ride. A quilted seat is fitted up and quilted on a light industrial sewing machine. You clip sheepskin down to a quarter inch or so, fit up the chap or garment leather over it, and chalk a design on the leather. After quilting is done, wipe off the chalk marks.

There are so many variations that one would, if he knew them all, need to publish a set of encyclopedias instead of a book. In fact I imagine most saddlemakers have a few tricks that others don't know.

I haven't said a word about tooling. We do make tooled saddles. But we have no room for it and there are many people far more expert on tooling than I who have written detailed books about it. Tandy sells those books. You do have to make special patterns for the saddles you work on. The fork cover is usually tooled after it's put on the fork. Other parts are tooled on the bench and then fitted up.

Repair Work

Repair work is usually a real drag for the saddlemaker. You lose money or clients. People bring you cheap saddles to repair; this repair, if your time is worth anything, will cost more than the saddle when it was new. Before long you'll know how to price. At first you'll get stuck. Actually, after you've learned how to make a saddle, repairing one is easy. The tough part is keeping the cost down.

Recently a man from a large dairy brought me a cheap saddle to repair. I took on the job as a favor.

The in-skirt rigging had rotted out. To adequately repair it, I'd have to put in new skirts—this would be very expensive. Instead I cut away the rotten leather, stitching where I cut. Then I put in a regular under-fork rigging, using D-rings.

The metal ground seat had been knocked down. It'd rub a horse, so I knocked it back up. I replaced tacks with ring shanks where the ground seat attached to the bars.

The horn cover was coming apart. I restitched it.

The stirrup leathers were rotten and the fenders were long gone. The saddle required new fenders and stirrups straps. I cut new latigos for it.

The saddle was caked with cow manure. I washed, oiled, and went over it with leather cleaner before I could stand working on it.

I charged the dairy a hundred dollars. Lost money on the deal. I don't think that saddle cost a hundred dollars when it was new.

When you have a chance to repair a fine custom saddle, you're in luck. Check it for new ways of doing things. You may find things you like in each saddle you work on. If you find pleasing saddle designs, make patterns of your own from them. Start doing this right from the beginning and keep it up. These patterns will save you a lot of time and effort.

Making an Uncomfortable Saddle Comfortable

You might get a lot of this work. Unfortunately, many saddlemakers don't ride their products, so the saddles never get tested until after they're sold. A very pretty saddle can furnish a terrible ride.

Paper pattern for padded seat.

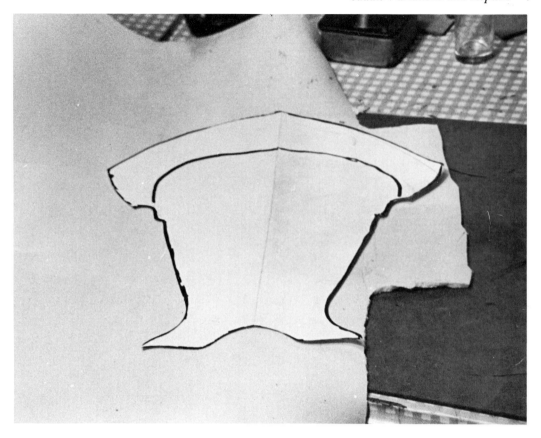

Place pattern on foam rubber.

Back about 1958 I made a saddle for a tall skinny cowboy. He told me he *had* to have a padded seat, but I scoffed. I told him I made such comfortable saddles, padding wasn't needed.

After a couple of weeks, the cowboy drove up. He had his saddle with him. It was rough side out, but there were two shiny polished spots on the seat, spots made by his fanny. As he had no padding on his rump, we finally had to put some on the saddle.

There are several ways to put in a padded seat. The main thing to watch out for is putting it on off-center. The actual seat resembles the body of a guitar. Look over some different padded seats in a saddle or tack shop. Pick out a design that you like.

You'll note that some are buckstitched and some are sewn. Some edges are pinked. They usually have foam-rubber inserts. A hard form is used for this. You can use sheepskin, but foam is better.

Probably the best padding today comes from Cris-Craft, the boat people. They sell huge rolls to the large saddle factories. Bill Porter steered me onto this. I contacted Cris-Craft and they sent me a sample—enough padding to do about 20 saddles. Boat shops and large saddlery supply houses should be able to supply you.

Cut a piece of garment leather to fit your measurements. Cut the foam smaller and back-bevel the edges for a smooth look and feel. Lay the foam on the seat, push it down, and check the fit. To make sure you're lined up, find the center

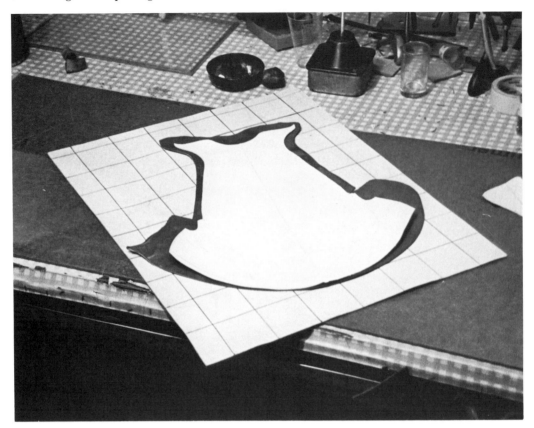

Cut garment leather a little oversized.

of the seat, mark it, and then mark the center of the foam. Take this down lightly while you fit the top leather piece.

Cut the top garment-leather piece a little oversized. Put it on the seat and check the fit. If all looks OK, mark the correct size and trim. Contact cement the pieces together. You should have a good fit if you've done all the measuring and marking with the padded parts in place. Make sure you leave enough garment leather to go up under the cantle binding or Cheyenne roll. Don't leave any tacks in place when you glue the pieces together.

If you're putting this seat on a saddle being repaired, you'll have to remove the cantle binding—Cheyenne roll—whatever. Remove the conchas and pull the seat loose. Make a pencil line where the padded seat will go, and rough the leather on the saddle seat. Also roughen the garment leather that will be cemented down.

You may want to pink the edges. If so, use a small pinking iron. Contact cement the seat down and go all over it with a leather smasher (an old doorknob will do), making sure the bond's good. Sew the edges by hand, by machine, or buckstitch. Rather than go into buckstitching, I refer you to books on the subject, generally sold by saddlery supply houses.

Put the seat back on and sew the cantle binding. If you want to quilt the seat, add a layer of clipped sheepskin. Sew the top piece of garment leather to the sheepskin. Clip the sheepskin down to about ¼ inch, using motorized clippers or regular shears.

Carefully draw your design on the garment leather. Chalk over pencil lines to make them easy to see. Sew by hand or take the work to someone who has a light industrial sewing machine. If you sew by hand, use a light linen thread rather than heavy nylon lacing. This thread comes in various thicknesses and can be purchased from Standard Saddle Tree Company or other saddlery supply houses.

When you have the seat off the saddle, take a long hard look at the ground seat. Compare it to ones you've done yourself. Padding might soften up the seat a little, but if the ground seat's bad, nothing will help except a new one.

Perhaps putting in a new ground seat's enough to make the saddle comfortable. Your corrective work shouldn't alter the fit of the seat enough that you'll end up with a sloppy-looking seat. However, if you've made extensive corrections, you might have to soak the seat and put it down as you would a new seat.

The fenders and stirrup straps usually wear out first. They are easily replaced. If you're supposed to match the old ones, however, the job can get expensive—you'll have to study the stamping design and duplicate it closely. Estimate your time and material, and charge accordingly. Only cut prices on a job like this when you're working on a top custom saddle. Then you want the job so you can study the saddlemaker's technique.

Of course the saddle owner may decide that plain fenders will do when he hears your price. In that case try to match the color of the original saddle. To dye a saddle, add dye to pure neatsfoot oil. The dye will soak in and have less tendency to rub off on clothing. Clean the dyed leather before the owner takes the saddle home, using saddle soap.

One big repair problem is restitching, which must be done by hand. Some saddles have had machine stitching put in at seven or eight stitches to the inch. Over the years the leather deteriorates, and if you used a machine to restitch, you might easily jerk out the leather between the stitch holes and mess up the job.

Use smaller awl points, needles and thread. Carefully check to see just what tension is needed to pull the thread. Don't enlarge the old holes; make doggone sure you run the awl point through at a 45° angle.

If the leather is too rotten to work, tell the customer that he'll have to accept it as is, or pay for replacement parts. This is the tough part about saddle repair. Few used saddles have had proper care. The rider will use his saddle until it's dried out—only then will he oil it. Next year it'll be dried out again and he'll re-oil it. After years of this poor treatment, the leather will rot. You can't do much with rotten leather. The leather on some old saddles tears away like cardboard.

Sometimes folks who don't know will bring you poor saddles for repair. A check of the tree will usually show that the canvas or fiberglass cover has disintegrated. The tree itself may be cracked or broken. Tactfully tell these folks that the saddle isn't worth repairing. Patiently explain why putting money into the rig would be a waste. In the long run they'll appreciate your honesty.

If you have a going repair business, you'll be located in a horsey area. There's good money to be made in halter and bridle repair. People who ride English saddles like leather halters. Horses do pull back and leather halters break. These folks pay a lot for halters and keep them in good shape. Most repairs are simple—just replacing or splicing a strap. Matching the leather is a problem. You have to use a good English bridle leather, which is finished on both sides.

I've had little to do with English-saddle repair. Most of the English-saddle work is replacing broken billets. You might have to loosen up the seat a little, match the leather, and sew new billets to the canvas up under there.

Most old western saddles need new sheepskin; moths damage the sheepskin of new saddles. Most of the work is getting the old skirts off, cleaning them, glueing the sheepskin on, sewing the edges, and putting the skirts back on. If you do a lot of such work, hunt up a sewing machine or take the saddles to a shop and have them stitched. You can really get into rotten leather when replacing sheepskin. Inspect a saddle carefully before agreeing to tackle the job.

Repairing Horn Covers

There are two ways to recover saddle horns—the cheap way and the right way. Quite often you'll keep yourself out of trouble by taking the cheap route. To do this, cut out the three horn pieces, put the horn cover on as described earlier (page 54), and fasten the wing ends down under the gullet. Of course the wings are outside the fork cover. If you put a latigo wrap on the horn, you'll cover up the wrap tails. Just cut the wings long enough to go down under the gullet.

The right way is to take the fork cover off, put the horn cover on as you would for a new saddle, and replace the fork cover. Getting the old fork cover off without ruining it is the problem. Remember, it's glued on. You have to take a screwdriver and break the leather loose from the tree. If the leather's in good shape, you can probably do it. However, you may stretch the leather even if you don't tear it, and getting it back on might be difficult. Explain the problem to the client and tell him you might have to make him a new fork cover. Or take the cheap route. It's his choice.

Repairing saddles and bridles that are silver-mounted can be frustrating if some of the silver's missing. Do your best to match it. Get a catalog from companies selling silver hardware.

Replacing a Broken Tree

Top tree makers will replace a tree for free if it breaks *on a horse*. Naturally, if you back a truck over the saddle, they won't replace the tree for free. The owner may have to pay for a duplicate tree and this service is more costly than buying a new tree.

If the saddle's in good shape, taking it apart isn't too tough. Just give yourself plenty of time to carefully cut the old stitches. You may have to ruin a part or two since saddle cement really holds. And you'll appreciate it if the maker didn't use ring-shank nails. When you can't get a nail or screw out, you can usually cut it out with a hack saw, hack saw blade without the handle, metal blade in a sabre saw, or a metal blade in a reciprocal saw.

When cutting the horn cover loose, cut through the first top piece that was nailed to the horn. This piece must be replaced so it's the one to ruin. Save the top and bottom pieces.

Just take a saddle apart in the reverse of putting it together. Conchas and strings are first. Skirts are next. Then comes the cantle binding and seat; cantle binding and filler. Loosen all the nails around the fork. Carefully break the old saddle paste loose with a screwdriver in order to loosen up the fork cover. Then you'll take the horn cover off to make slipping the fork cover off easier. Gullet cover and ground seat are last.

When you put this stuff back on the new tree, clean and (or) oil each piece. Dirty leather can be cleaned with oxalic acid, then saddle soaped. If the saddle's tooled, a final protective coat of Resolen or some other leather finish will make it look almost new. The appearance of such work is important.

Cincha Making

The main reason we make our own cinches is that the supplier might be out of what we want. Or we might have to wait too long to get what we want. If we make our own, all we have to do is order up a supply of cinch cord and cinch buckles.

Some of the fancy cinches hurt horses, especially after the cinch gets stiff and dirty. Folks do use dirty cinches. Over a period of time horse sweat makes cinches very stiff and hard.

Wash cinches in a machine by putting them in a cloth sack, such as a navy ditty bag. Or wash them by hand in a bucket.

Dirty and puckered center bars on cinches make many horses sore. I favor a leather center bar sewn on the outside of the cinch, which can't form lumps and hurt the horse. When a horse has a permanent lump from bad cinches make a cinch with side bars and no center bar. This spreads the cinch cords out around the lump. Of course, you can't fasten anything to such a cinch.

I made a frame to make cinches on. The top bar can be raised or lowered to make cinches of different lengths. When a cinch is finished, I remove it and put new cinch buckles in place—all ready for the next one.

You can buy buckles and mohair hanks from Standard Saddle Tree Company. They come in lengths to make a 19-strand cinch or a 21-strand cinch. I like a flat plate cinch buckle—the #302. This is a three-inch cinch buckle. Normally you put 19 strands on it, but if you make wider cinches, you need a wider buckle. I've put 25 strands on a $3^1/_2$-inch buckle.

Start at the center when making cinches. Use a cinch knot to secure the mohair to the cinch buckle. There should be about five feet of cord left on each end when you're finished tying on the cord.

There are many ways to finish up the cinches. I learned a simple way that works well and this was home discovery. Alan Dewey looked at a good cinch and figured out how to duplicate it. It may not be too perfect but it works.

Start with four strands of mohair twisted to make one working strand. Cut three of these strands about four-inches from the buckle. Then weave one strand in and out just over the cinch knots. Next half-hitch the strand around each strand of the cincha; pull tight. Throw half hitches going to the left when you're working to the left; throw half hitches to the right when you're working to the right. Make a double half hitch where you end up, and start back.

If you're doing a nice cinch, you may want to half hitch back and forth a couple inches up the cinch. Then you start dropping the end strands until you're approaching the middle. Leave about an inch or longer in the middle when you finish. The working strand you're half-hitching with may not be long enough to complete the work. Take one of the strands you previously cut off, weave it around a few strands and half hitch over it with the old working strand. Then continue half-hitching with the new working strand. Putting in this splice is very easy. When finished, I use a large needle such as mill workers use for sewing grain filled sacks. I make my needle from a piece of stiff wire. The end is heated and bent around to form the eye. The eye is ground smooth on my knifemaker's grinder and soldered together with low temperature silver solder.

This tool, poked through the woven work, catches the working strands and lets me weave them back and forth and secure them. You lay the cord in the tool's slot and shove it through the weave. Pull the end out tight. Then stick the tool back through a bit farther down, pick up the strand and pull it back towards you. A little bit of this secures those loose ends.

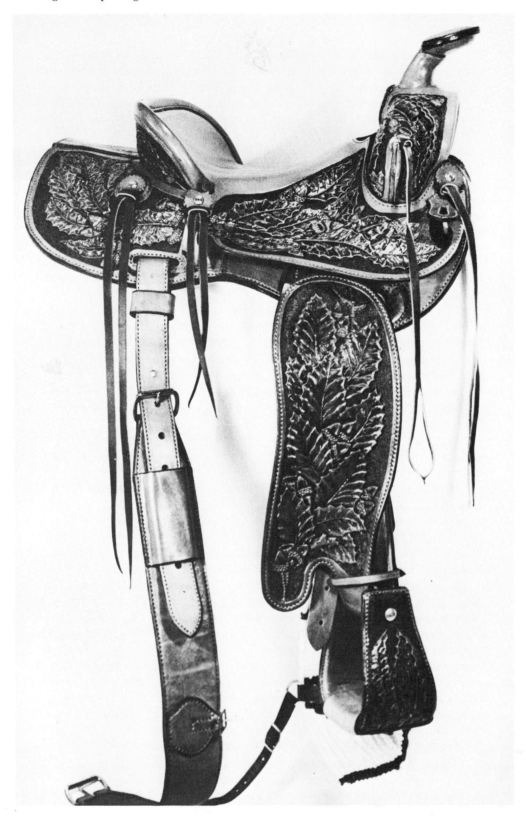

Tooled saddle with standard stirrup slots. (Made by Dave Jones.)

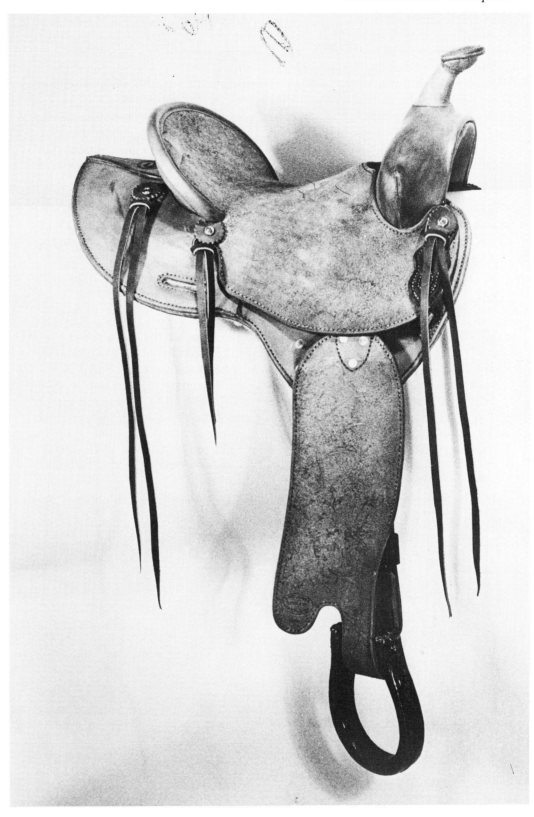

Barrel racing saddle. (Made by Dave Jones.)

Now for the center bar. I mark the center of the cinch with a felt-tipped marker and run one length of sewing thread through at the center. This holds everything in place for it's easy to cross one strand over the other and mess up the cinch. Take the cinch off the frame.

Cut the leather for the center bar. Scrap latigo is fine for this. Set in a couple of D-rings. I double it all the way. I contact cement it together.

The worst problem I had with this was getting the whole works to the stitching horse without having it slip out of place. My best solution to date is to contact cement the leather to the mohair. Of course, this won't hold much. It does allow me to get it clamped in the stitching horse without slipping. It's then a simple matter to securely stitch it.

Lately I've been sewing leather keepers for the half-breed off latigo on the cinches. My old boss, Charlie Araujo, had some cinches fixed like that and it works well. To give yourself room to sew on a two-inch keeper, you need to half hitch about 3–3½ inches down the cinch. The left side is finished like any other cinch, dropping strands as you finish up.

Breast Collars and Bridles

Sometimes clients want you to make bridles and breast collars to match their saddles. Good ones are doubled and stitched. You split the leather to a uniform size. Latigo or lace leather makes a good liner. The easiest way to get things shaped up to stitch is to cut the liner larger than the bridle leather. Contact cement them together and trim off the surplus leather with a round knife. Bridles are usually sewn six or seven stitches to the inch. The breast collar should match the bridle so use the same number of stitches on it.

It saves time and leather to make up patterns to work from. When you see something you like, make a pattern of it. Patterns you want to keep can be made from light poster paper.

If you have a lot of such work to do, better hunt up a good sewing machine.

4

Final Notes and
List of Suppliers

One who hand stitches all his saddles is, of course, interested in the best sewing thread available. I'm very pleased with a polyester thread made by Ludlow Textiles, PO Box I, Ludlow, MA 01056. It's called Waxed Polyester Handsewing Thread (LP1546). It comes in white, black and brown colors. After oiling a saddle, the thread retains it's color.

At present, it comes in sizes #4, 8, and 9. The #4 is all right for fine work but a little light for general saddle work. The #8 is a little heavy but it's fine where 5 stitches to the inch are used. A #6 would be about perfect and this would be made if enough people became interested in it.

There are other companies making poly thread. The Leather Factory, 3080 St. Elmo Ave., Chattanooga, Tenn. 37409 handles a poly thread somewhat more limp than what Ludlow makes, but it works. Mid Continent Leather Co., PO Box 4691, Tulsa, Okla. 74104 (800-331-9134) also sells this thread.

The flat waxed nylon lacing commonly used for hand stitching is also made by Ludlow Textiles. I consider the round poly thread superior in every aspect for the saddlemaker. It makes a better tapered end, doesn't pull off the needles, and is far less prone to piercing by the needles during hand stitching.

A saddlemaker suggested that I contact an expert tool maker for a basket stamp I needed. I'd heard of him before and I think he made my saddle stamp for me. I contacted him and bought a couple of round knives that are the best I've seen. His name is Ellis Barnes. His address is Box 7–B, Elfrida, Arizona 85610. His telephone number is 602-642-3891. I ordered a pair of cantle pliers, a basket stamp and a swivel knife.

Some time ago, I bought a Gomph draw knife/draw gauge and the quality of this tool is outstanding. Mr. Barnes owns Gomph Leather Tool Co. and the Ray Hackbarth Leather Stamp Company. He makes tools with old time quality one just can't find today. Top leather craftmen such as Al Stohlman, Ray Pohja, Cliff Ketcham and Bob Beard all use his tools.

Ellis Barnes made his first tools in 1940 while working as an apprentice at Ed Bohlen's shop in Hollywood, California. He was soon selling tools to top craftmen. In 1980, Ellis moved from Los Angeles to his native Arizona where he

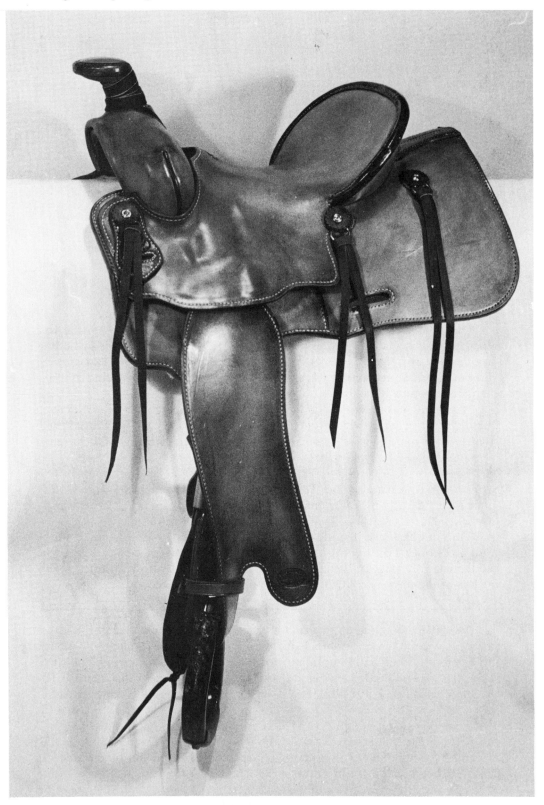

This saddle has the doubled (turned) welt and a rawhide horn rim and rawhide cantle binding, both of which are becoming popular. The thread used for the stitching is the waxed polyester.

continues to make fine tools. He offers a full money back guarantee and says he's had but one round knife and one stamp returned—not because of poor quality but because of price. Since top quality tools are always a bargain, we should expect to pay for the best. Ellis says, "Quality is remembered after the price has been forgotten."

After talking with many top saddlemakers, I've found that they lack good edge bevellers and French edgers. There is only one size French edger currently being sold in mass quantities in the United States. The more leatherwork I do, the more uses I find for French edgers. My English buddy managed to get a complete set for me from the Joseph Dixon Tool Company. He also got me a complete set of edge bevellers, a blunt-nosed tool that will bevel edges in tight corners.

The Schillers (Barry, Carol, and son, Mike) of Campbell-Bosworth Machinery Co., have moved to Ft. Lauderdale, Fla. In addition to the machines, they have made a deal with the Joseph Dixon Co. to stock their fine leather working hand tools. You can get French edgers, edge bevellers, etc. from them.

Mike Schiller
Leather Machinery Corp.
Address and phone number
found on page 41 of this
book.

Carol Schiller
Campbell-Bosworth Machinery Co.
720 N. Flagler Drive
Ft. Lauderdale, Fla. 33304
800-327-9420
305-463-7910

Treemaking, like saddlemaking, comes in spurts. One tree company may be very busy, taking, say, eight months to get a tree for you. It's a good idea to check with other treemakers to get an idea as to delivery time. Of course, you may find that you like one company better than the others.

When a treemaker takes the time to explain the various bars he uses, you'll have a better idea what to buy. Wade, west coast, Arizona, Rowell, Hamley, etc. are all types of bars. Ask the treemaker for his opinion about this.

Standard Saddle Tree Co.
PO Box 674
Provo, Utah 84603
801-373-0355

Hercules Saddle Tree Co.
702 S. Main
Moab, Utah 84532
801-259-8106

Ritter Saddle Tree Co.
Star Rt. Box 100
Anthony, New Mexico 88021

Hal Simpson Co.
2714 Walnut Street
Denver, Colo. 80205
303-292-6520

Here is a list of suppliers for all of the equipment mentioned in the book.

Campbell-Bosworth Machinery Co.
Address found above

Chuck Collins Custom Silver
P.O. Box 667 Oakland, OR 97461

Silver suppliers.

Colorado Saddlery Company
1631 15th Street
Denver, CO 80202

Suppliers of Dexterine

Custom Knifemaker's Supply
P.O. Box 308
Emory, TX 75440

The company that provided me with my
sander-grinder.

Alan Dewey
127 West Cunningham
Grangeville, Idaho 83530

Maker of deep throat stitching
horses and leather tooling stamps.

Diablo Manufacturing Company, Inc.
P.O. Box 1108
Grass Valley, CA 95945

Silver suppliers.

Flanagan Saddlery-Hardware Corporation
370 McLean Avenue
Yonkers, NY 10705

Golliger Leather Co.
PO Box 6660
Glendale, CA 91205

A leather warehouse.

Herman Oak Leather Company
4050 North 1st Street
St. Louis, MO 63147

A tannery.

L.B. Lienemann
625 Grand Avenue
Billings, MT 59101

An excellent knifemaker.

Make It with Leather magazine
2715 West 7th Street
Fort Worth, TX 76107

B.P. Marshall
103 East Louise
Lathrop, Calif. 95330

Makers of deep throat stitching
horses

Montana Silversmiths
PO Box 839
Columbus, Mont. 59019
800-548-4511

Silver suppliers.

Sachs-Lawlor
1717 South Acoma St.
Denver, Colo. 80223

Saddler's stamps can be found here.

Sholze Tannery
3100 St. Elmo Avenue
Chattanooga, TN 37408

Standard Saddle Tree Co.
Address found on page 119

Suppliers of trees and other equipment.

Texas Leather Company
P.O. Box 123
Yoakum, TX 77995

Texas Saddle Hardware
Route 1, Box 170
Joshua, TX 76058

Silver suppliers.

U.S. General Supply
100 General Place
Jericho, NY 11753

Suppliers of miniature power tools

Walsall Saddlery Hardware Corporation
7831 East Greenway Road
Scottsdale, AZ 85260

Supplies old-fashioned awl hafts.

Woodcraft Supply Corporation
313 Montvale Avenue
Woburn, MA 01888

Supplier of the Beechwood spokeshave
and hand felt wheels.

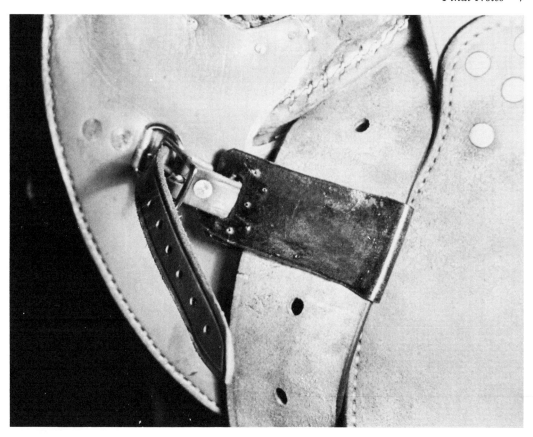

The stirrup leather holder, bind, and D-ring set in the skirts.

My saddlemaking is mostly concerned with the special tree I use with the forward stirrup straps. A great many riders want the ride my type saddle gives them. However, you can't use my tree with a double bullhide cover nor can it be used with the new thin flat "cutting boards" that are popular today. I recently worked out a "gimmick" that a saddlemaker can use to get the stirrup straps forward on any western saddle, though it works best on saddles that are rigged in the skirts.

This gimmick is a form of "binds" that are used on rodeo bucking horse (association) saddles. A problem with regular binds is that they bend the stirrup leathers, which leads to cracking and breaking.

The method I use is to employ a rawhide piece that holds the stirrup strap and allows it to be pulled forward. The rawhide is about 3½-inches wide by 8-inches long. It's shaped around a piece of scrap leather about 3⅛-inches wide. When the rawhide's dry, I varnish it. There's a slot in the front of the rawhide wide enough for a ¾-inch strap. I put a reversed D or rectangular "square" in the saddle skirt at the front, about where a ring or slot for the breast collar would go. A strap allows the stirrup strap to be drawn forward just as far as the rider wants it. This is a real asset on a long ride, for the position of the stirrup straps can be changed for comfort.

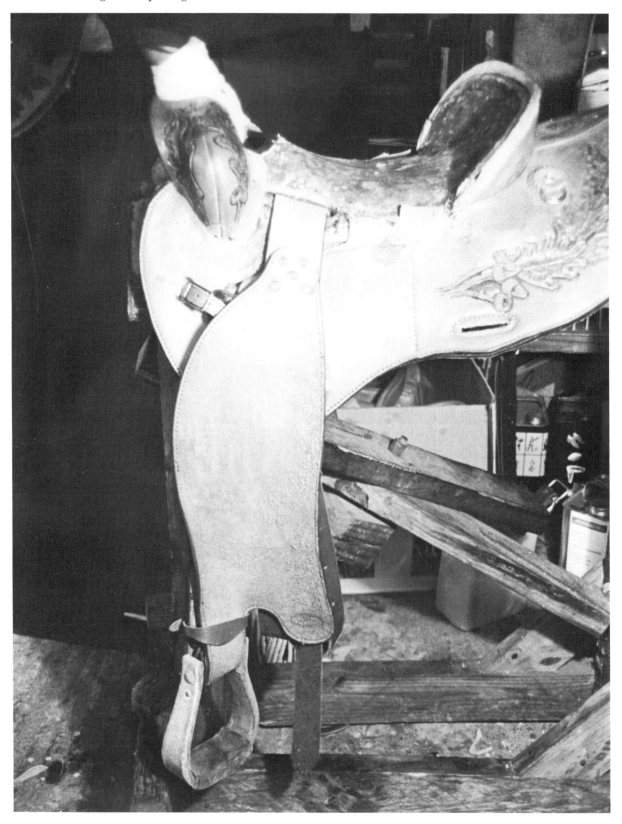

The "bind", showing the place it's put in and the effect it gives.

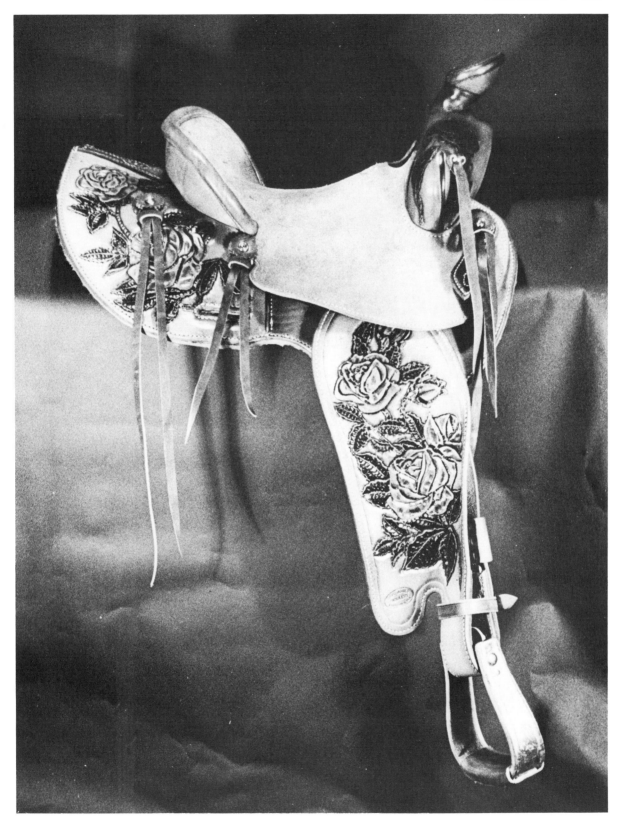

Another saddle with the rawhide binds. Notice how the stirrup strap is pulled forward. It can be pulled as far forward as desired.

After some practice you should be able to build a nice saddle. There are variations from the saddle I made, but these differences can easily be worked out—they concern design and rigging.

Before starting a saddle project, it would be wise to make some bridles, breast collars, and halters. This would give you practice using your tools, making waxed ends, sewing, etc. You might try to do some low-cost saddle repair to get the hang of it. And this would start your pattern collection. Get some catalogs. Get some other books.

Ask questions. Try to make friends with those who already make saddles. You might check out current saddlemaking schools. This is the way you grow in ability and knowledge.

There's nothing like personal experience working for a saddlemaker. Maybe you could work in a shop on your vacation from your regular work. If you worked for nothing as a janitor, you'd still profit from the experience of watching a saddlemaker work.

No book can tell you everything. If you work at saddlemaking all your life, you'll still have a lot to learn. Consider this book as a tool to help you start. If it's a help to you, I'm grateful.

Now let me talk about something I know little about; namely, sewing machines. I have investigated them a bit. A sewing machine eliminates a lot of work. With a machine, the saddlemaker could do more work on a saddle, such as sewing around the seat and fenders in addition to the skirts.

There are a lot of good machines but most saddlemaking machines haven't been made for years. These are awl and needle machines. The awl punches a hole ahead of the needle, so tighter stitching will result. Machines such as the Landis 16 and the Randall are fine but very expensive if you can find them at all. I hear talk of the Landis 16 selling for $6,000 to $7,000.

> For machines: The Randall Leather Machinery Corp.
> 33-01 Hunters Point Drive
> Long Island City, NY 11101
> 800-223-6018
> handles Union Lockstitch
>
>
> Campbell-Bosworth Machinery Co.
> Address found on page 119

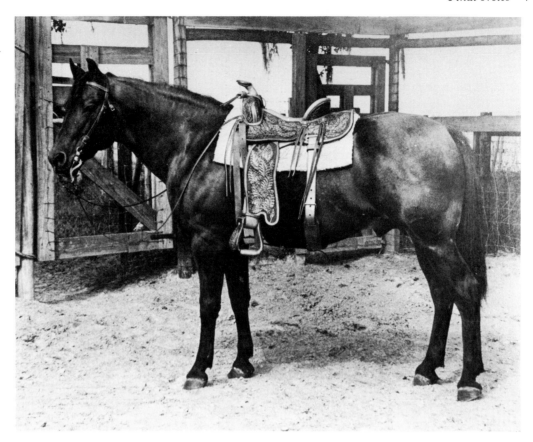

Trying a new saddle on Tengo Tivio.

My aim has been to give the reader some place to start from. I hope you will find the places to get your tools, leather, and tree. And I hope that you will then have some idea of how to go about the business of making a saddle. With time and ability, you'll go on.

Index